Touching the Mountain

THE SELF-BREEMA HANDBOOK
Ancient Exercises for the Modern World

by Dr. Jon Schreiber, D.C.

Illustrated by Mary Cuneo

California Health Publications

Oakland, California

All inquiries should be addressed to:
California Health Publications
6201 Florio Street, Suite 1A
Oakland, California 94618
Telephone (415) 428-1283

Cover photography:
Front: Galen Rowell/Mountain Light
Back: Michael Irwin Photography

International Standard Book No. 0-9623581-2-6
Library of Congress Catalog Card Number: 89-85099
Printed in the United States

Touching the Mountain

"The root of all health is in the brain. The trunk of it is in emotion. The branches and leaves are in the body. The flower of health blooms when all parts work together. The fruit of health grows when they work together purposefully. Health produces seed when the purpose is achieved."

—Kurdish saying

ACKNOWLEDGMENTS   Many people contributed their time, creativity, and expertise to the creation of this book. Many others gave inspiration, and many more were simply very supportive. To all of these people, sincere thanks. Also, I wish to thank every student who walked through the doors of The Institute for Health Improvement during my many years as a student there, and everyone who has been a patient at Schreiber Chiropractic Natural Health Center.

Special thanks are due to: Manocher Moviai, Susan Varner, Mary Cuneo, David Curry, Gretchen Brandt, Judith Meites, Ann Hudson, Janet Madden, Don Cohen,D.C., Janet Chann, Robin Somerville, Whitney Riter, Joanne Sultar, Christine Hunt, Marian Clark, Roxanne Schroter, Jean Haseltine, Sharyn Venit, Diane Burns, Grace Moore, Christie Ahlf, Don Davidson, D.C., Peter Hensel, Jan Winitz, Matt Schreiber, Tatjana Kopp, Irene Newmark, C.A., Susan Green, D.C., Eliane Walis, Jon Lobdell, Celeste McLean, Bill and Frances Schreiber, Karen Burt-Imira, M.D., Marc Ams, Aron Saltiel, Franci Gallegos, Mrs. D.C. Warlow, Peter and Beth Lisker, Ariel Youst, Susan Weiner, Liana Rodegard, Ann Mattingley, Michael Irwin, Rafael, Lois Huish, Ron Romack, Michael Evans, Nik Kleinberg, Jerome Weitz, D.D.S., Joshua Rosenbaum, Arthur Ogawa, and Pari Schneider.

DEDICATION I wish to thank all those persons and influences, both known to me and unknown, who have helped me come to a point in my life where I could participate in the making of this book. Special thanks are due to instructors and staff members at The Institute for Health Improvement and of Schreiber Chiropractic Natural Health Center, where the exercises and the principles inherent in them have speeded the recovery of many hundreds of patients and students.

May these exercises benefit others as much as they have me. The Breema method helps prepare the soil for the seed of unfolding health and self-development. Through our own efforts and supportive natural forces, that seed can have the possibility of sprouting.

DISCLAIMER Self-Breema was developed by people who had profound insight into the structure and function of the human body. The exercises are an expression of the natural and universal laws which govern the body and its health. The reader must carefully apply the exercises and their underlying principles to his or her personal condition, using caution and common sense.

The book is designed to provide enough information to enable the reader to learn and do Self-Breema safely. Please be sure to read the chapters entitled "Applying Self-Breema to Common Health Problems," "Self-Breema and Health Improvement," and "A Word on Back Problems."

This book is sold with the understanding that the publisher and author are not engaged in rendering medical or other professional health services via the book and its contents. The purpose of this book is to educate you, and to encourage you towards self-education. Consult a health professional if you have questions or problems. The author and publisher shall have neither liability nor responsibility to any person or entity with respect to any loss, damage, or injury caused or alleged to be caused directly or indirectly by the information contained in this book.

PREFACE For hundreds of years, the exercises in this book have been passed down directly from one generation to the next. They were integrated into the daily life of the people using them, and conformed to their daily needs. The exercises are now presented for the first time in written form, treasures from a remote place and age. This book is the chest that holds these treasures.

How can you find the keys that will unlock this chest, to make the treasures your own? The first key is your willingness to practice and experiment with these exercises.

To retain some of the power and freshness of the oral tradition, the book is designed to be read aloud, preferably with a partner, unless you have already witnessed a presentation of the exercise. It is also possible to learn and practice the exercises at The Institute for Health Improvement in Oakland, California, where the form and atmosphere of the oral tradition is continued. In addition to Self-Breema, the Institute teaches Breema bodywork, a form in which treatments are done with a partner. Certified instructors of these practices may also be available in your area.

Jon Schreiber

Contents

I am very pleased to see the authenticity with which these exercises have been captured, for the first time ever in their long history, on paper. My wish is that everyone who practices Self-Breema have a taste of its full benefit. A phrase I often use may help point you in the right direction:

"When I am alive,

when I am alert,

when I am connected to the common sense and instinctive nature of my body,

whatever I do is Breema."

Manocher Movlai

Founder, The Institute for Health Improvement

Introduction

EFFECTS OF THE EXERCISES

The exercises in this book are selected from a large collection of individual and partner movement sequences called Breema bodywork. Through their effects on the energy system of the body, Self-Breema exercises have an unlimited capacity to release tension, increase relaxation, and foster vitality.

The most immediate aim and result of Self-Breema exercises is to support and balance the flow of life energy in the body. This takes place, to a great extent, through what we know as the acupuncture meridians. These meridians are a set of 14 channels connecting the hundreds of acupuncture points identified by Oriental medicine with each other and with the internal organs of the body. Blockage in the flow of life energy along these meridians and imbalance between nurturing "yin" energy and stimulating "yang" energy are held by Oriental medicine to be the principal causes of tension, weakness, and other disease-precipitating conditions in the body.

By working directly to support and balance life energy, Self-Breema nurtures the body. It can also produce tangible effects such as release of muscle spasms, life extension of intervertebral discs, relief of arthritic pain and reversal of some of its degenerative changes, and stimulation of the circulatory system. Other potential benefits include cleansing the lymphatic system, harmonizing and tonifying the digestive system, and improving musculoskeletal dexterity, emotional balance, and mental alertness.

HISTORIC ORIGINS   The Kurdish village of Breemava is located high in the mountains that separate Iran from Afghanistan. Due to its remoteness and the traditional independence of the Kurds, the village has remained insulated from the major events that molded Afghanistan and Iran.

The people of Breemava are primarily farmers and shepherds. They have developed a sensitive and innovative relationship with nature that allows them to create abundance in a stark and arid environment that most people would find hostile and even uninhabitable. Their daily routine requires ingenuity and hard work. Both men and women participate actively in village life. A person's position in the village hierarchy is determined by his or her personal achievement or wisdom, as well as by family history and age.

Through those who have left Breemava for long periods and returned, the villagers, though immersed in their daily world, have become familiar with the concepts of Islam, Judaism, Christianity, and Buddhism. Most do not feel bound by any religious teaching, but use whatever they experience as valuable in their daily lives.

These features are common to many Kurdish villages. What makes the Breemava villagers unique is the bodywork they practice, which is based on a set of exercises and movements developed over centuries. Although the early origins of the practice are unknown even among the villagers, this much is certain:

- The exercises were often inspired by the everyday movements of people following a simple lifestyle close to nature, such as harvesting wheat or churning butter.

- Although several families figured prominently in maintaining the teaching tradition of the bodywork, any person attuned to the body and the Breema method could propose, develop, and refine a new exercise or treatment.

- Many individuals are remembered by the villagers for the quality and extent of their contribution to the body of Breema treatments and Self-Breema exercises. One of these was Diyeh Bonneh ("Mother of Light"), who specialized in nurturing or "yin" Breema treatments. Another was a man named Khalu Cammereh, whose sequences are characterized by a subtle rhythmic component.

- Over time, the Breema exercises, treatments, and principles were incorporated into the day-to-day life of the villagers as important means for sustaining their bodily and mental health, happiness, and self-development. In this way, the functions of medical, church, psychological, and public media services in a more modern society were combined.

The common sense wisdom that governs Breemava activities encourages not only material production, but the development of each person's potential. Thus, even though young people, as usual, gravitate toward those jobs for which they have particular talents, they are often required to perform jobs for which they have little aptitude or liking, until mastery of the task is demonstrated.

HOW BREEMA CAME TO THE WEST

Even in his later years, my grandfather never mounted his horse by climbing up gradually. Somebody asked him, "Why do you always jump straight into the saddle?" "I hate to figure out which foot to put in the stirrup first!" he replied.

For centuries, the Breema method was practiced only by the inhabitants of Breemava. Few outsiders knew of the existence of this village or its remarkable bodywork system. Although the people of Breemava have never sought to extend the influence of the Breema method beyond their small village, they are neither secretive nor proprietary about it. The village's isolated position has served to keep Breema an unhidden secret. There are visits by people from the surrounding area, who arrive accompanied by a sick or injured relative. The person in need of help is brought to the village elder, and then receives one or more Breema treatments. Self-Breema exercises, nutritional advice and herbal remedies, and any other necessary measures are prescribed and taught.

In the mid-1950's, a young man named Manocher Movlai left Breemava, after spending the first seventeen years of his life there. His childhood had proceeded much as that of any other villager. He studied Breema bodywork informally as a little boy, absorbing as much as possible of the atmosphere and practice of Breema. He often did Self-Breema exercises with his brothers and sisters, friends, and adults.

At the age of nine (along with the other village boys and girls), his "formal" classroom training in Breema bodywork began. Daily, and sometimes several times a day, they were taught by the village patriarch, who was Manocher's maternal great grandfather. "Grandfather," or "Khan Baba," as he was called there, was the recognized authority on Breema, and was directly related to Khalu Cammereh and the other notable contributors to the Breema method. He was known for his abundant vitality and his great wisdom in all matters relating to health.

Manocher often spent time with Khan Baba outside the classroom. At these times, Khan Baba went out of his way to give Manocher a practical education in applying the principles of Breema to the activities and situations of daily living.

Soon after Khan Baba died, at well over 100, Manocher left Breemava. He travelled and lived for many years in the Near East, Middle East, and Europe. He also made several trips to the U.S. For over two decades, Manocher studied methods of health improvement and healing from all over the world, and researched the effects of different cultural and societal conditions on health. His work brought him into close contact with many famous and many undiscovered masters of various healing methods and disciplines, including authorities on modern allopathic medicine.

A questioner by instinct, Manocher at first doubted the value of his childhood training as compared to Western health practices. Yet as a result of his experiences, he came to see that Breema offers something essential that is either unavailable or very difficult to achieve through other methods.

Specifically, it could provide a practical framework for health improvement and maintenance that can lead to a more harmonious, less stressful life, particularly in modern Western countries, where the simple truths of health have ceased to be common knowledge.

In response to this potential, and after more than twenty years of developing and refining formats most suitable for conveying the essence of the Breema method to Westerners, Manocher founded the Breema Center for the Healing Arts, in Berkeley, California. Years later, it was renamed The Institute for Health Improvement, and moved to its present location in Oakland, California.

During the past nine years, Manocher has worked extensively with a core group of instructors, teaching them the Breema method in depth, and preparing them to teach it in the traditional format. Special emphasis has been given to those aspects which are most important for people who live in modern Western societies. Together, Manocher and the Institute's instructors have taught Breema to hundreds of students, and have certified many practitioners and instructors.

Manocher continues to teach advanced classes in Breema bodywork, Self-Breema, and the practical philosophy upon which the Breema method is based. In addition to teaching classes and workshops, he maintains an active supervisory role at the Institute, ensuring that the teaching remains pure in both form and principle.

THE LANGUAGE OF THE BODY

A seed may be created in the mind, but can only be nurtured in the heart.

Ordinary language is attuned to mental concepts, symbols, and word meanings, a predominantly left-brain function. Self-Breema can teach you the language of the body, a more right-brain activity that operates best while the ordinary mind is "in neutral"— not classifying and judging every experience.

Each Self-Breema exercise has been exactly designed for its potential to create a specific experience in your body. A very similar experience will occur for anyone who does the exercise correctly. By tuning in to the experience that is created in your body by the exercise, you will become sensitive to the language of the body: how it expresses its needs and its true reactions, free of mental suggestion. As you learn the language of your body, you will know what type of movement your body is calling for at a particular time. You will know precisely how fast to do that exercise, how long to hold positions, and how to move, without having to think about it.

Self-Breema can teach a common sense understanding of the body, an intuitive understanding, that is constantly being fine-tuned by the feedback received from the body in the form of sensed experience. At that point, you can really start to work *with* your body, rather than against it or in spite of it. One simple exercise can then have a profound effect on your physical health and on your emotional and mental well-being. Your body is no longer wholly at the mercy of your mind and feelings. Instead, you have the possibility of making it your faithful friend and ally in life.

And how it will serve you! It will work harder, better, and with less back-talk in the form of sluggishness, exhaustion, tension, pain, illness, and disease. Maybe you didn't realize that these, too, are parts of the language of the body, messages which we constantly receive.

From an even broader perspective, one can regard most forms of movement and dance, certainly all the performing arts, as means of expression for the body. However, this simple aim can become secondary to the aim of impressing an audience. What is lost most quickly by this shift in emphasis is the second-by-second *experience* of the person doing the dancing or moving, as their attention is diverted from the internal to the external aim. One can then easily become deaf to the body's language.

NURTURING VS. STIMULATING EFFECTS

The master called his student to him and said, "I will impart to you the greatest wisdom existing: You are surrounded by Life!"

The whole universe supports your existence. Nearer things (air, food, sense impressions) usually have a more obvious effect, while the effects of more distant things (planets, stars) may be more subtle.

One way of classifying these effects is as either predominantly nurturing or stimulating, equivalent to yin or yang in Eastern thinking. For example, your alarm clock rings (stimulating), you step into your woolen slippers (nurturing), have a cup of coffee (stimulating), listen to the birds singing (nurturing), are narrowly missed by a car as you cross the street (stimulating), stand at the bus stop and notice the sun's warmth on your body (nurturing), remember an unpleasant task you need to perform at work (stimulating), and so on through the day.

Activities that you enjoy doing are particularly nurturing, especially if they involve some creative input on your part. Their primary objective is not outside reward or approval, either financial or other, but rather the personal satisfaction they bring you. Common examples include painting, preparing food, repairing a watch, even organizing your closet—almost anything you throw yourself into wholeheartedly, and invest some of your creative energy in.

Nurturing and stimulating events have different effects on the two parts of your autonomic (automatic) nervous system. The sympathetic part of the autonomic nervous system acts on the body to prepare it for intense activity, through mechanisms such as release of adrenalin into the bloodstream. The parasympathetic part governs functions such as rest, regeneration, digestion, detoxification, and growth.

Stimulating events tend to activate the sympathetic nerves, while nurturing events tend to activate the parasympathetic nerves. The best balance for good health and personal growth appears to be nurturing for 80% of each day and stimulation for 20%.

Now try timing the events of your day according to whether they are predominantly nurturing or stimulating. If you are a typical person, you will probably have the figures reversed, with 80% or more stimulating, and only 20% nurturing.

What does this mean in practical terms? It means that our lives are out of balance, either through circumstances or by our own choice of activities. What are the results of this imbalance? It can mainifest in many ways. Worry, anxiety, tension, headaches, ulcers, obesity, heart disease, and cancer are some of the undesirable results of overstimulation, or undernurturing.

What is the solution? It's certainly not to quit your job and spend the next few months in bed. Too much nurturing, and too many sudden changes in your life, can be as troublesome as overstimulation.

More difficult but more rewarding is to learn how to *balance the effects of overstimulation* through *bringing more nurturing experiences of a transformative type into your daily life*. The aim of this strategy is not to escape from your surroundings and activities, but to transform your inner state so that your surroundings and activities nourish you.

Usually, people try to change their energy state in a way that is ultimately harmful to them. Someone who feels nervous, hyperactive, or negative might have a few drinks, take a pill, or watch television.

These methods can certainly change one's energy state, but they tend to be passive rather than active, stimulating rather than nurturing, and to operate by draining one's "excess" energy. This energy was at first disharmonized through overstimulation, which created an undesirable state of the body, mind, or feelings. Now the energy is drained, and with its disappearance, the immediate problem seems to disappear, too. Now, however, this energy is no longer available to you. Looked at in this way, it would be preferable to redirect your energy rather than to get rid of it.

Where does Self-Breema come in? Self-Breema exercises can have a profoundly nurturing effect that helps to create or invite a complete change of state: from closed to receptive, from sluggish to vital, from hyper to calm, or from depressed to joyful: in short, from identification to presence. This beneficial effect on your energy state is a by-product of attempting to do an exercise correctly (which includes registering its effects).

To go back and refine our original statement of aims, Self-Breema exercises work by balancing the movement of life energy in your body, bringing movement to energy which is blocked, and relaxation to tense areas. Energy, like water, stagnates or evaporates when it is still, leaving some areas dry and others too wet; and like water, movement purifies it and keeps it fresh.

How can a single exercise bring both relaxation and stimulation to the body? It can, because the more nurturing or yin types of Self-Breema have an element of stimulation in them, and the more stimulating or yang Self-Breema retain an underlying nurturing quality. They can balance the energy of your body because they are themselves balanced activities. That's why one short exercise can have such a positive effect.

SELF-BREEMA AND HEALTH IMPROVEMENT

Every person is born with a particular innate level of health, and into a particular environment, which, depending on its attributes, can nurture or damage health.

The single most important factor in creating and maintaining good health is your own effort. This simple and obviously truthful statement appears radical because society has taught us that health can be purchased by accessing medical assistance. Even rudimentary self-help health measures have been virtually lost to us, because they are seldom passed down within families or in schools. Most of us know little more about what to do about our health than what we see advertised.

While a doctor or other health practitioner can help tremendously, a "you-can-do-it-all for-me" attitude is misleading, and reflects ignorance of the nature and component elements of health. A more truthful statement would be, "I wish to become healthier *with your help.*"

The Breema method views health as a function of the practical wisdom of the body. By becoming receptive to the body's instinctive wisdom, and then experiencing it, that wisdom becomes available to help us. When it is *acted* upon, instinctive wisdom becomes practical wisdom. Sensitivity to our own instinctive wisdom can be fostered by sources outside of ourselves, as well as from within ourselves.

So it is possible to benefit by the practical wisdom of other people, and other health practitioners. Their experiences with health improvement, especially their personal experiences, could help others to awaken to and act upon their own instinctive wisdom, helping it to manifest in the form of good health. This help from outside can be given in many ways, including through sound advice, emotional support, medical or food substances, impressions, atmosphere, touch, and exercise, to name just a few.

The billions of dollars spent by unhealthy people seeking relief have not gone unnoticed, and have pointed out a need that many in the health and helping professions, and many lay people, are responding to, each to the best of his or her ability. Open-mindedness and a sharing of the great wealth of useful medical information, accumulated by many diverse health practices over thousands of years, is needed. From this can come a synthesis, a new medicine, based on certain fundamental laws and principles, including:

- Respecting the structural, physiological, and chemical integrity of the body wherever possible;

- Augmenting the natural healing abilities of the body with natural substances wherever possible;

- Restructuring social priorities to decrease or eliminate some of the life-threatening situations and health hazards that have become an accepted part of our daily lives.

Self-Breema did not develop solely as a physical health improvement method, but more as a method of bringing the body into balance—internally by harmonizing the mind, feelings, and body, and externally by attuning the practitioner with his or her environment. Yet, these seemingly subtle effects are of great value in health improvement. Clinically, we have selectively prescribed and taught Self-Breema exercises therapeutically to thousands of patients at Schreiber Chiropractic Natural Health Center over the years, with unquestionably positive results, for problems as diverse as sciatica, premenstrual syndrome, headaches, and asthma, to name only a few.

And as emphasized elsewhere in this book, great health benefits can result from the initiative taken by students of these exercises, as they try to apply the inherent principles to the physical form.

In Self-Breema, form and principle unite, allowing health to pass through oneself fresh and new each moment, in the form of vital life energy. Health means aliveness. To Life!

ORGANIZATION OF THE BOOK The next two chapters deal, respectively, with the physiology of the body and with certain general principles and suggestions for doing Self-Breema. We strongly recommend reading these chapters; they will increase your understanding and enjoyment of the exercises, and may also prevent injuries. The remaining chapters of the book consist of sets of Self-Breema exercises that are appropriate for learning and practicing together. Each exercise in a set is complementary to others in the set, so that each set done together utilizes a variety of body parts, muscle groups, movements, and tempos.

The exercises in the first group, forming introductory Set A, are chosen both for their relative simplicity and for their ability to illustrate a variety of basic positions, postures, and movements. For this reason, we recommend that you begin your practice with exercise Set A.

You can also make up your own sets of exercises for a session, based on specific health benefits or other objectives. For this purpose, the exercises are listed in Table 1, which indicates which parts of the body tend to be utilized in each exercise. You can also refer to the chapter entitled "Applying Self-Breema to Common Health Problems." The emphasis of each exercise is explained in the comments just preceding its instructions.

Physiology

Self-Breema works with four of the body's most important subsystems: the musculoskeletal system, the meridian system, the hara, and the sarkhaneh. We conclude with a chapter on back problems, because of their prevalence and their high responsiveness to appropriate Self-Breema exercises.

MUSCULOSKELETAL   *The most valuable force exists in wisdom, not in muscles.*

The musculoskeletal system includes the bones, muscles, tendons, ligaments, and all the body's joints. Together, they give the human body its distinctive physical shape. From a functional perspective, the interrelationship between these parts permits and defines movement.

Healthy bones are dependent upon good blood circulation to supply them with organic and mineral nutrients and structural elements, and to carry away metabolic waste. Bones are made of living, changing cells, and so need constant access to the body's blood circulation.

Bones are exercised and strengthened by two main types of forces: those that compress them (bearing weight, lifting and carrying things), and those that pull on them (via muscles and tendons). Without these stresses, bones will atrophy, as happens to astronauts who spend a lot of time outside a gravitational field.

Muscles, tendons and ligaments, like bone, need healthy circulation, need to stretch beyond their normal resting state, and need to tighten or constrict as well as stretch. Most modern sports and exercise plans emphasize the constrictive aspect of muscular movement and under-emphasize the stretching aspect. Thus we are accustomed to thinking of someone with tight, hard muscles as strong. Muscles, however, are a much greater asset when their strength is accompanied by their ability to stretch.

Joints are the areas where bone meets bone, and articulated movement is accomplished. Where bones form joints, they are usually covered with a smooth cartilage and enclosed in a fluid-filled capsule. This delicate synovial fluid is the body's motor oil, protecting and lubricating the joints.

Several conditions make for healthy joints. The ligaments that connect the bones at joints must be strong but not too tight, in order for the bones to stay aligned in relation to each other. Any misalignment will mean improper movement, which can cause wear and tear on the joint, with eventual disease and breakdown.

The joints should be used frequently, and taken through their complete range of motion in a relaxed, natural manner. Otherwise they will become restricted in their movement or degenerate. The old saying, "Use it or lose it" is very applicable.

The joint fluid must be supplied with proper nutrients by a wholesome diet and healthy digestive system. If circulation is inadequate or if the eliminative organs are not functioning up to par, the joint fluid may become a storehouse for toxins. This, in turn, can lead to irritation, swelling and arthritis.

How does Self-Breema affect the musculoskeletal system?

It affects the bones by gently putting them through a range of compressional, stretching, and torsional movements. Muscles are stretched slowly, safely, and gently, allowing for real increases in flexibility. The natural postures and movements of Self-Breema can help to realign the joints, allowing smooth, easy movement.

Most importantly, Self-Breema promotes natural synchronization among the functions of the muscles, bones, joints, and the respiratory, circulatory, and nervous systems. When Self-Breema is done properly, no part of the body is overworking. Each supports the other. This results from using the whole body to accomplish every movement, however slight. In this way, the body is retrained to work and move as a functional whole, naturally seeking out postures and movements that involve the whole organism, not just an isolated part of it. Thus the chances of injury, either acute and sudden, or slow and degenerative, are reduced.

Self-Breema can teach the musculoskeletal system to work with less interference from itself. The end results are less tension and more vitality.

YIN AND YANG   *A man went to a famous samurai and said, "I had a dream. In my dream, my father told me to challenge you to a sword-fight." The samurai looked at him and said, "Well, you had your dream. Wait until I have mine."*

Understanding Self-Breema in terms of Oriental medical thought requires first some familiarity with the Chinese concepts of yin and yang. Yin and yang are the opposing or complementary qualities that result from the creative manifestation of indivisible being into the physical and energetic worlds, where there are no absolutes and where everything exists as parts of a whole, not in isolation.

We could start with the Western folk saying, "Every stick has two ends." It illustrates the complementarity of yin and yang, and how both together define a larger whole. The corresponding Chinese saying would be that "everything has two features," but it would go on to claim that one of the features has more yin qualities, and the other more yang.

The word yin originally referred to the cooler, shady side of a slope, and yang to the warmer, sunny side. Yin includes qualities such as rest, nurturing, downwardness, contraction, and decrease. Complementary yang qualities are activity, stimulation, upwardness, expansion, and increase. The terms are relative: warm is yang in relation to cool, but yin in relation to hot. Equally as important as the basic definition of yin and yang is the idea that they constantly create, regulate, and are transformed into each other. For example, it is easy to see that temperature is created by phenomena manifesting through the opposing qualities of heat and cold; and that the interaction of heat and cold controls the temperature; and that temperatures nearly everywhere are constantly changing, even though they may seek a particular point of balance in a regulated system such as the human body.

You have surely noticed other examples of complementary features; how rest follows activity, how solitude creates the need for social contact, and the way night always follows day. Once you start looking, it is possible to see that all phenomena in the world of space (yin) and time (yang) are a blend of such opposites.

The ancient Chinese knew that for yin, the receptive, feminine, inwardly directed, earth type of energy to be balanced, it needed to carry a seed of yang, the sun principle, with active, masculine, outwardly directed attributes, and vice versa. We see this graphically in the yin-yang symbol (☯), where the two energies within the wholeness of the circle are each shown to be defined by the other, to contain the seed of the other, and by the implied motion of the line through the center, to constantly transform from one into the other.

MERIDIANS Meridian is the English translation of a Chinese medical term for the dynamic channels that convey life energy (ki or chi) between the organs and the exterior of the body. This energy flow nurtures all parts of the body, including bones, tendons, and joints, as well as regulating the balance of yin and yang energies in the body.

Meridians are usually named after the organ that they are most closely related to. They are grouped in yin-yang pairs. The seven yin meridians, running up the front of the arms, legs, and torso, are called lung, spleen, heart, kidney, pericardium, liver, and conception vessel. The corresponding yang meridians, running down the back of the arms, legs, and torso, are the large intestine, stomach, small intestine, bladder, triple burner (for the upper, middle, and lower thirds of the trunk), gall bladder, and governing vessel.

Disorders anywhere along the course of a meridian disturb the flow of energy, and therefore the yin-yang balance, throughout the meridian. The two major modes of restoring balance, according to Chinese medicine, are herbal remedies and acupuncture. In acupuncture, designated points along the meridians are treated by insertion of fine needles. About 2,000 acupuncture points have been identified, of which about 150 are likely to be employed by a single doctor. Repeated studies have confirmed the efficacy of herbal and acupuncture remedies.

Virtually the entire surface and interior of the body are traversed by one or more meridians. For this reason, the stretches, leans, taps, brushes, and other moves in Self-Breema also actively influence the flow of energy in the meridian system. The wide variety of movements and postures in Self-Breema are specifically intended, among their other benefits, to balance the energy flow in all of the meridians.

HARA *In Kurdish, they say, "**First** fill up the water jug. **Then** you can have a drink."*

Viewed from a Breema perspective, the hara is perhaps the most important area of the body.

In Breema and Self-Breema, the hara corresponds to the entire abdominal area. Physically, it is bordered above by the rib cage and below by the pubic bone. The analogous area on the back is also considered to be hara, as is everything inside the body between these borders. In Japanese medical philosophy, the hara has its epicenter two finger breadths below the navel.

All energy meridians of the acupuncture/acupressure system pass through the hara, either directly or via their internal connections. This alone shows the importance of the hara, as all parts and systems of the body can be affected here. Breema has its own meridian system, different from, but not conflicting with the Oriental system. In Breema, it is said that all meridians both begin and end in the hara.

In addition to being the "Grand Central Station" of the meridians, the hara houses most of the body's organs. Any Self-Breema exercise that affects the hara can have a direct effect on these organs, especially those of the digestive system. In Oriental medicine, a properly functioning digestive system, particularly the colon, is considered a necessary base for physical and emotional health and strength. For these reasons, the hara is called the center of vitality.

There is a saying in Breemava, "*Bandeshowal* is the cure. All the ghosts, all the shadows, they're afraid of *bandeshowal*." *Bandeshowal* is the the rope with which people in Breemava secure their pants. So when someone is afraid, they grab their belt-knot, thus bringing their hand to the hara. The result is strength and clarity, making the "unreal" disappear.

Structurally, the hara area is the body's center of gravity. Thus we have the concept, key in both martial arts and in Self-Breema, of "moving from the hara." By bringing the attention of the mind to "connect" with the hara, one experiences a feeling of groundedness, or connection to the earth. This is easily observed in some people from Oriental, Mid- and Near-Eastern cultures, who seem to walk from their bellies. How different from typical Westerners, whose minds are absorbed with random thoughts and preoccupations, oblivious to the existence of the rest of their bodies, and who walk with the head leading, giving the impression that their bodies are simply a kind of vehicle, transporting the head from place to place.

Breema bodywork treatments often work directly with the hara, because "hara work" is so direct and penetrating. The hara is often held with a receptive or "mother" hand while the active hand works with another area of the body. Here the hara is being used as a connector of various body areas, somewhat analogous to a chakra, or energy center in the ancient Indian systems.

How does someone who has never before worked with the concept of hara begin? There are many Self-Breema exercises designed to foster a connection with the hara. All Self-Breema exercises encourage full natural breathing, which by its nature involves the hara. Physically contacting the hara itself is also a good way to direct the mind's attention there.

One of the simplest Self-Breema exercises is called Holding Hara. It is a wonderful practical introduction to hara. Here are the instructions, so you can try it now:

- Sit in seiza position (kneeling).

- Hold the hara with the right hand, and hold the left hand on top of the right. Take three breaths, as you "breathe into the hands" (imagining that your breath flows in through your palms as you inhale).

- Brush the hands down to your lap.

The Breema method considers the hara to be extremely perceptive and sensitive. People in Breemava weigh the substantiveness of another's words by the effect they have on the hara. Echoes of this wisdom are evident in English sayings like: "That didn't sit well with me." The hara is also very sensitive when it comes to touch. It doesn't like an insecure touch, nor does it want a rough touch; it appreciates the proper blend of firmness and gentleness, applied through the natural weight of the relaxed, "unself-conscious" hand. It is under this touch that the hara lets go of its protective guarding and becomes the energy reservoir that is replenished as it is drawn from.

SARKHANEH *Someone asked a master, "What is the highest level of development one can attain on Earth?" And the answer was, "To **BE** on the Earth!"*

The sarkhaneh refers to the areas on the right and left sides of the chest just inward from the shoulder joints and just below the collarbones. Each sarkhaneh is about the size of your palm.

The sarkhaneh (the Kurdish word is both singular and plural) is a very important area in both Breema treatments and Self-Breema exercises. Its name poetically means Source of a Thousand Oceans, Gate of a Thousand Oceans, and Source of Wisdom. The Sarkhaneh contain the first point of the lung acupuncture meridians (Lung-1), which is of tremendous significance in Oriental medicine, and whose Chinese name, Zhongfu, means central residence. Many ancient religions have prayers and rituals that involve holding or striking the sarkhaneh in supplication.

Structurally, the sarkhaneh overlie the superior lobe of the lungs and an area richly endowed with lymphatic channels. Superficially, the sarkhaneh is covered by the pectoralis muscle. So by working with the sarkhaneh, one can nurture, stimulate, and detoxify the lungs and lymphatic system. This is a big aid for anyone with upper respiratory or lung problems, as well as for everyone who has to breathe polluted city air. Work with the sarkhaneh strengthens the immune system. The sarkhaneh can also help in healing shoulder joint and scapular injuries, because muscles that pass through the sarkhaneh affect these areas.

Energetically, the sarkhaneh are connector points that distribute and balance the energies of the heart and hara. As a result, sarkhaneh work can calm and balance the emotions.

A WORD ON BACK PROBLEMS

There's an old Kurdish saying, "When you pour muddy water into the most beautiful cup, it still tastes bad. But when you pour fresh spring water into an old cup, no matter how beat up, it tastes great."

To illustrate the usefulness of Self-Breema for a particular type of problem, and to provide some cautions on the use of the exercises, we'll comment briefly on back problems, defined as injury or pain between the base of the neck and the hip joints. Much of the same reasoning will apply to other muscle groups.

It is usual to distinguish three basic causes of back problems:

- Congenital or hereditary predisposition;

- Macro-trauma (car accidents, falls, etc.);

- Micro-trauma, from long-term repetitive movements, or postural imbalances.

Often two and sometimes all three of these causes contribute to a back injury.

If you have a back injury or a history of back trouble, you need to be extra careful with all of your activities, including exercise.

Self-Breema is the most complete exercise system for the treatment and prevention of back injuries of all sorts that I have ever encountered. A series of specific Self-Breema exercises, including many of those in this book, is used routinely to help patients at Schreiber Chiropractic Natural Health Center heal their injuries and strengthen their back muscles.

Many of our patients have had serious injuries. Many have tried everything else and come to us in desperation, hoping to avoid surgery or stop the use of pain-deadening drugs. Some come after unsuccessful surgeries. In nearly every case, Self-Breema offers a simple-to-do, step-by-step road to healing back problems, especially when used in combination with Breema bodywork treatments.

In other words, far from being a reason to avoid exercise, back problems create a strong need for exercise, both to effect a cure and to prevent recurrences. Self-Breema provides a safe and organized method for the care and prevention of problem backs. By following a few simple principles, it will be very difficult to damage your body doing a Self-Breema exercise:

- If you have a back problem, respect the current limitations of your body. Pain is a message from the body that says "don't do it." By completing 5% of a Self-Breema movement without pain, you benefit far more than if you do the whole exercise while feeling pain.

- When your back is hurt, move more slowly. Make the effort to follow your body's movements with your mind. This way there are fewer unpleasant surprises.

- Nurture your body by minimizing stimulating foods (sweets, oils, caffeine, meat, refined grains, added salt, dairy products), increasing raw and cooked vegetables, and eating lightly. Sleep on a firm surface. Take a hot bath once a day.

- Minimize the time spent sitting in chairs. Allow your body to walk or stretch when it calls for movement.

- As you heal, increase the number and variety of Self-Breema exercises that you do. Make a habit of doing some stretching exercise just before bed and on arising.

These simple, time-tested rules can have a profound effect. Give your body a little nurturing and its healing powers will amaze you.

Principles

SUGGESTIONS FOR PRACTICE *A student of the Buddha asked him, "How did you become what you are?" Buddha's reply was, "I took the first step."*

In this chapter, we present some advice from experienced Self-Breema students and instructors that can help substantially in your own practice of the exercises. Briefly, they are: find a partner and appropriate space; find an interest in your mind; register the connection created between the body, and mind and/or feelings as the exercise proceeds; seek a balance between form and comfort; and above all, remain a beginner, approaching each repetition of the exercise as if for the first time, with an interested mind and an open heart. These principles, in fact, apply to many types of activities, and you may find that their practice in Self-Breema exercises will carry over to other actions that you need to take in responding to the demands and opportunities of life.

Find a Partner and Appropriate Space

If you are learning these exercises from the book for the first time, it will be much easier to have a partner read the instructions aloud, straight through, slowly and distinctly, as you perform the movements. Then come back to any unclear parts for special practice, looking at the illustrations as necessary. If you have no partner, read what you can retain and then do the movements referred to.

The best indoor surface for doing Self-Breema is a well-padded rug on a wooden floor. It is also very supportive to have natural light and living plants in the room. An outdoor location is an attractive option, especially near sunrise or sunset.

Find an Interest in Your Mind

When your body has weight, you are lighter than air.

The more your mind is interested in what you arc doing, the more attention you will have for the exercise. To start this process, we suggest bringing your attention to the fact that the body is breathing and has weight, at the outset of each exercise. The effort of bringing the attention to the body will harness the mental energy that is usually spent on daydreams, worry, and criticism in which the mind loves to engage. Gradually this energy is made available to the body, which can become vitalized and filled with life energy.

Your feelings, which are normally preoccupied by reactions of attraction to or repulsion by everything the mind presents to them, are influenced by the new energy created through this mind-body alliance. The feelings usually respond by becoming calm and supportive of the mind's interest in the body.

The mind will be tempted to think that it has learned an exercise once the component movements are fixed in short-term memory. This is a necessary but superficial part of the total learning process. Only the *experience of doing* Self-Breema repeatedly teaches the body *how to do* Self-Breema, as in the motto "learn by doing."

Register the Effects of the Exercise

*My grandfather used to tell me about a mountain called **Peh-ro**. He explained it in a way that made it seem alive. Once he said, "All I can do is explain the color of the stones, the size of the mountain, how many steps it takes to get to the top, how it curves and slopes, what plants and animals are on it. I can explain the totality of that mountain for you. But understanding comes when you climb it."*

A fundamental goal of Self-Breema is to create movement that is natural to the organism, movement that, with the participation of the mind as an active observer, can kindle and enliven the feelings. This produces a unified activity in which the body, mind, and feelings can all participate fully.

The supply of energy made available by the harmonious activity of mind, feelings, and body can cleanse, balance, and energize every cell in your body. Your part in the exercise now broadens to include *registration of the effect* of the exercise on your body, mind, and feelings: an extension of what was said earlier about the language of the body.

The more subtle benefits of Self-Breema all come from looking for and registering the effects of each Self-Breema movement. In this way, one can learn how to do Self-Breema attentively, not like a machine, picture-perfect but bland. The heart of Self-Breema is in tasting the experience of each Self-Breema exercise, each time it is done.

Seek a Balance Between Form and Comfort

*A great master died and went up to heaven. At the gate he met Saint Peter, who, just as a formality, checked the list of those eligible to enter. The master wasn't on it. "That's strange!" they both said. He checked again. No master. How could that be? He went through the list again and again, and searched everywhere. No master. "Well," said the master, "could you check the list of those who **can't** enter heaven?" Saint Peter checked, and, sure enough, found his name. "Aha!" said Peter. "Here you are. It says, 'Reason: Never broke any rule.'"*

When doing Self-Breema, you need to practice receptivity, experimentation, and sensitivity. Your aim could be to approximate and decipher the form while maintaining the balance in your own body, even if this requires some compromise of the exact form.

An attitude of acceptance towards your present condition is a big aid. It allows you to take an accurate look at yourself, without denial or grandiosity, and frees you to progress from your present capabilities to what you wish to become.

An attitude of acceptance makes it unimportant how flexible you are when you first begin Self-Breema. I know! I used to be famous for having the stiffest, most rigid body around. No amount of stretching exercises helped me. Only when I finally let go of my self-criticism, which evidently was adding to the tension, did my body begin to change. Self-Breema was the vehicle that slowly but surely transformed my body.

If you stretch your body well beyond its comfortable limits, it hurts. You might be injured, and you will certainly not find the thought of repeating the painful position enticing. Moreover, pain and fear of injury create tension, and tension creates stiffness and constricted breathing, exactly opposite to the results that you want. Breathless concentration is a good way to create a muscle spasm.

Mullah Nasser Eddin is a legendary Middle Eastern wise man. Stories about his escapades are often told in Breemava. This short anecdote says a lot about the results of force.

> Mullah Nasser Eddin was walking through a field when he came upon a man beating a cow. "Why are you beating her?" asked the Mullah. "Well," replied the man, I used to have a horse who could carry three times as much as this cow can!" "Thank you," said the Mullah. "Why do you thank me?" asked the man. "Well, I never before knew that by beating it, I could turn a cow into a horse!"

Self-Breema exercises cannot be done with excess tension. Even if the movements are correct, you are not doing Self-Breema, only mimicking their external form. It is far better to "cheat" on the form itself and remain comfortable, while your body relaxes and gradually adapts to the form. More precisely, in a "stretchy" Self-Breema, you could stretch up to a comfortable relaxed limit, then 1% more, and hold the stretch for an extra breath. Also, please avoid: 1) bouncing motions to increase a stretch; and 2) stretching to look good.

Self-Breema is done for yourself, not competitively, as we may have learned other forms of exercise. The competitiveness that began with sports has spread to some health and fitness exercise. When winning becomes more important than staying connected with one's body, the risk of injury and the need for medical care are increased. Instead, try to make relaxed exercise a habit.

For some persons, certain postures or movements are uncomfortable or even impossible. If you find that you are unable to do a particular exercise correctly, it's fine to adjust the form in order to be comfortable. In fact, if you need to tense your body or ignore pain in order to do a Self-Breema form precisely, you are no longer doing Self-Breema. But try to be as true to the exercise as you can, without denying your own limitations.

The flip side is that accepting the present condition of your body can help open the road to health and well-being. Bit by bit, as your body gains in flexibility and becomes more comfortable with the exercise, you can start to follow its form more precisely. Flexibility is not the aim of Self-Breema; it is one by-product of doing something in which the body, mind, and feelings all participate fully and equally.

Remain a Beginner

*In Breemava, it is said, "The joy of the little boy who **doesn't know** is **much** more real than the superficial pleasure of the old man who plays wise."*

In any endeavor, a correct attitude is the first requisite. Since the aim of Self-Breema is experience of oneself rather than simply performing a physical movement, the correct attitude is that of a beginner. Then, the experience can be totally fresh each time.

Why is this so? A beginner doesn't start with the attitude, "I already know this exercise, it's easy, so I don't need to pay close attention." A beginner is curious, eager to learn from each repetition, and so cannot afford to do things automatically while his or her mind wanders. A beginner has a sense of mystery about the present moment and the next moment, relaxing the fixed expectations and boundaries imposed by the ordinary mind. A beginner's attitude enables the benefits of understanding to increase with each repetition. Even after a thousand times, we can still be receptive to what is available for us in the movements.

Receptivity is the most important attribute a person can have. Via receptivity, development is possible. And it is exactly this receptive quality that creates the attitude proper to a beginner. Not only is a beginner more open-minded, he or she is open-hearted. This means that the emotional energy is more available, both to participate in one's activity, and to be affected by that activity. This "energy of the heart" is needed in order for us to be affected constructively and correctly.

When you are a beginner, you have enough wisdom to know that real knowledge is a product of the moment, not simply the acquisition and collection of past data. A beginner wishes to experience the momentary effect created and given by Life. And that, in fact, is the only experience of real value possible for us.

To sum up, it is only the *experience* of doing Self-Breema that is valuable and that can teach us how to do Self-Breema, not the memorization of the movements, as in an academic subject. Moreover, without your presence in the experience, you can be doing the moves perfectly from an outsider's view, and still not be doing Self-Breema at all. But with a beginner's attitude, whatever you do is Self-Breema.

HARA AND CONNECTION TO THE BODY

*If you could shape your life by **thinking**, you would have done it by now!*

Del-aka, the Kurdish word for hara, indicates an area without a precisely defined physical location or rigidly demarcated boundaries. Consistent with this meaning, Breema practice emphasizes the *experience* of the hara, instead of focusing on its definition and description.

In the Breema method, we say, "connect to the hara" as a shorthand way of saying "start to intentionally create a state of focused attention from which it is possible to *connect to the body*." However, the body you can connect with is not the one you have in your mind. That which the mind thinks this body is, actually is only the mind's *image* of this body. If we say "connect to the body," you may connect mentally to that image, which, of course, is not your actual body.

When we say "connect to the hara," the mind, hopefully, does not have a definite pre-formed image of the hara. Therefore, it doesn't already think it knows, and so may become a bit more receptive. The possibility is created for *actual* connection with the body. Connection to the body is an *experience*. This experience has a definite physical quality, a "taste." That taste cannot be experienced by the mind. It cannot be created by thought. When the mind tries to have the experience, it creates tension in the body, and then the registration of that tension is erroneously labeled "connection to the body." Connection to the body has nothing to do with tension.

It comes when the body is free of unnecessary tension, when the mind is working intentionally (or is quiet but available), and when the feelings are receptive and supportive of the body and the mind's activity. This unity of the body, mind, and feelings has many degrees and varies in duration, yet always creates a common "taste." Words can't adequately describe this taste, but its attributes include a sense of calmness (even during intense activity), clarity, physical strength, and "groundedness." Connection to the body begins with the body in its natural state, without unnecessary tension. The mind can register the experience, but is not the "experiencer." If the experience itself does not take place, the mind works with fantasies instead of reality, and *imagines* that it is experiencing, according to its hypothetical images. So the mind may think it has a body to connect to, but that "body" doesn't really exist. When we ask new students: "Are you connected to the body?", they invariably say "Yes!" They check with their mind to see if they are connected to its image of the body, and the answer in the mind is "yes."

After practicing Breema or Self-Breema for a while, the false authority of the part that said "yes" eventually disappears, as you get a taste of your actual body, instead of your imaginary one. This experiential taste is the foundation for establishing a genuine inner authority.

At this stage, when you ask yourself, "Am I connected?", the answer is usually "NO!" There is much more substance in that "No" than there was in the earlier "Yes." When you say "No," you *know* that you are less identified with your mind's image of the body.

By experiencing the body in its natural state and by connecting to the hara, we can come to the experience of connection to the body. By connecting to the body, we become open to the intelligence of the common sense of the body, or what is called "the instinctive wisdom of the body." It is this wisdom that can lead us toward understanding how to maintain health in the body and well-being in our lives.

And remember that the first step is the most important: Connect to your hara.

RECURRENT MOVES AND POSTURES

Several movements and postures that are used repeatedly in Self-Breema exercises merit some general explanation, in order to avoid repeating detailed instructions each time one of them is encountered. The ones we will explain at this point are standing, sitting, brushing, leaning, lowering the arms, and holding. It's important that they be done comfortably and correctly. You may want to practice them in advance of encountering them in the individual exercises.

Standing

Many Self-Breema exercises begin or end in a standing position, which to an observer appears like an ordinary, relaxed posture. The feet are shoulder-width apart, arms at the side, hands hanging open. From the "inside," we suggest the following additional features of the standing posture: notice that your body has weight, and that the weight is equally divided between the two legs; register that the floor or earth is supporting your weight through the feet, and that your body is supporting the weight of the relaxed arms, shoulders, head, and neck; notice any areas of tension or discomfort throughout the body, along with the overall sensation of the body; and register that the body is breathing.

When you find your mind drifting away from these efforts, register that also, without criticism, and ask it to return to its job of noticing the body standing. This is a good way of either beginning or continuing a connection with your body.

Our point is that the standing posture is part of the exercise, not a "time out," and so not an invitation for the mind to wander.

Please note that *all exercises* end with an instruction to sit or stand comfortably. The ending position is a transition, either to another exercise or to another activity, and a time to assimilate or digest the results of the exercise. A transition of two or three breaths' length is suggested.

Sitting

The remarks for standing apply to sitting, which may take one of two forms in these exercises: sitting with the legs crossed in front of you ("sit with legs crossed"), or kneeling. Kneeling is usually referred to by the Japanese term "sitting seiza" (prounounced **say**-za). In kneeling, you are sitting on your own heels, usually with the knees apart for added stability. Either of these positions may be uncomfortable at first, but with practice, the necessary muscles and tendons will become more flexible.

Sitting seiza is at first difficult for some persons because the ankle joints are not flexible enough to allow the feet to plantar-flex so they can be folded underneath the body. However, it is well worth the effort. The benefits of sitting seiza include a high degree of spinal flexibility, as the weight of the head and torso is distributed very naturally into the hips. The floor supports most of the body's weight, leaving the spine and sacrum free to come into a more natural alignment that provides a sense of balance and solidity. Children all over the world, grownups in cultures with few chairs, and people with low back pain are natural beneficiaries of the position.

If you are not yet comfortable in a seiza position, try a pillow under your knees, try sandwiching a pillow between the back of the thighs and legs, or sit seiza for short periods at a time. Your body gradually will grow accustomed to it, and may eventually come to prefer it. However, if an exercise in this book calls for the seiza position before you're comfortable with even a modified position, you should sit in any way that is comfortable. If necessary, you can even sit in a chair.

Brushing

There is a poem that says, "I discovered the secret behind the beauty of the flowers. They open wholeheartedly."

Many Self-Breema exercises involve "brushing" the arms, legs, feet, or other body parts. Brushing generally has a nurturing effect, and allows the physically active parts of an exercise to have an even more deeply penetrating effect on the body. If you omit the prescribed brushing in an exercise, you will likely experience a feeling of incompleteness. Try it again, this time brushing, and see if you can feel a difference.

Brushing is done with the fingers and hand totally relaxed, molding to conform to the contour of the body part being brushed. The more complete the contact between hand and part being brushed, the greater the effect. Sometimes even the forearm makes contact while brushing. There is no need to use any pressure whatsoever; the natural weight of the hand and arm is always enough.

One should always brush as if the *whole body* is doing the brushing, not just the hand. As a background aim, you should ask that every cell in your body participate in the process of brushing.

Brushing is intended to be simple, pleasurable, and above all, a totally natural physical expression. It is *not* a process of intentionally redistributing energy, or of getting rid of "bad" energy, and it is therefore not necessary to "shake off" anything in the process. It is also not for outward show, because Self-Breema is intended to help one travel from the imaginary to the reality of the body.

The efficacy of brushing can be traced in part to its balancing effect on the body's meridian system, tonifying or sedating the flow of life energy in the meridians according to need. The meridians are extremely sensitive and are influenced by the slight pressure exerted by the natural weight of the brushing hand and arm, as well as by the heat radiated from the palm. They also are influenced by the small electrical currents induced by the relative movements of charged elements in the bloodstream of the brushing hand.

Leaning

"Leans" on parts of the body in Self-Breema are generally done with an open hand that conforms, as in brushing, to the shape of the part which you are leaning on. The idea is to transmit weight from one part of your body to another, with minimal expenditure of energy. No muscular force is used; instead, your body's weight does the work. The leans are slow and even, with the same length of time spent in releasing the lean as in applying it. When leaning progressively down a limb or other body part, the increments of distance are usually small, so that several leans are required to cover the whole of the limb.

Leaning, like brushing, tends to follow the acupuncture meridians of the body, and for this reason has a direct nurturing and releasing effect on the flow of life energy in the limbs and their joints. This effect is enhanced by the regular rhythm with which the lean is applied. Because the leaning is done by you to yourself, you are in the position of being both practitioner and recipient. You can explore this idea by noticing both types of effects: the receptive or yin effect on the "recipient," and the more active yang experience of the "practitioner."

Lowering the Arms

In many Self-Breema exercises, the arms will be raised to a position straight overhead, usually at the end of an inhalation, and then be allowed to lower slowly and evenly out and down to the sides. The aim is to have a continual experience of the pull of gravity. The uniform rate of descent can vary each time you do the exercise, but for any one time, the rate, once chosen, should not change. The result is the balancing of two opposing forces: your muscular energy and the pull of gravity. Each helps you to experience the other more fully, which can help to produce an experience of your own body.

The instruction will be simply, "lower the arms to the side," or "allow the arms to lower to the sides," but implies the indicated method of lowering, not to (for example) let the arms collapse absent-mindedly, or to bring them down energetically or erratically.

Try now raising your arms over your head, then lowering them as suggested, emphasizing the evenness of the movement, and see if you can get a sense of how the whole body is involved in this simple process. Then repeat the movement, this time watching for unnecessary tension in the arms or shoulders. Think back to this experience sometimes when doing other movements, and notice if they have the same feeling of evenness, freedom from unnecessary tension, and involvement of the whole body.

Holding

Some exercises either include or end with a hold: both hands held over the hara, or the heart, or the eyes, for example, usually for three breaths. This requires two comments. First, like standing and sitting, the holding is a part of the exercise and warrants your close attention. In fact, when the body is physically at rest, there is an opportunity to take stock: what is the effect on my body of the preceding activity, and of this hold? Holds are very nurturing to the body and a useful contrast to active movements. Energetically speaking, they are like "closing a circuit" that includes the hands, the arms, the hara, and the part of the body being held.

Second, whenever breathing is referred to in Self-Breema exercises, we mean the normal breathing of the body, without forced inhalation or exhalation. Some exercises include instructions for coordinating movements with inhalation or exhalation, and many exercises have a rhythm that will naturally synchronize with breathing. For example, usually bending forward sharply will coincide with the desire to exhale.

HOW TO START EACH EXERCISE

*There is a saying, "Someone who can do one thing well can do everything well." But that **well**…*

There is something that you must do before each Self-Breema exercise. It is an integral part of every Self-Breema, but does not appear in the written instructions, in order to save space. It is assumed that once you know it, you will do it every time you practice an exercise.

Every Self-Breema begins with three breaths:

- First breath: Inhale, and as you do so, experience the effect of inhalation on your upper body (the hara, and everything above it).

- As you exhale, experience the effect of exhalation on the lower half of your body (the hara, and everything below it).

- Second breath: Inhale, experiencing the effect of inhalation on your whole body. Exhale, experiencing the effect of exhalation on your whole body.

- Third breath: Inhale, and as you do so, experience the joy that accompanies the inflow of life energy that comes with inhalation.

- Exhale, experiencing the vitalizing effect of exhalation on the body.

This preliminary breathing will enable you to do each Self-Breema exercise better. The mind, feelings, and body are primed for coordinated, cooperative activity. The necessary receptivity is created, so that Self-Breema can have a more penetrating and beneficial effect on you. Now you're ready to begin.

HOW TO READ THE EXERCISES

The instructions for each exercise are accompanied by numbered illustrations. Numbers indicating the appropriate illustrations appear at various points in the text. Where the drawings continue onto a second page, the corresponding instructions are reprinted, in italics.

Just enough drawings accompany each exercise to make the instructions clear — not every step is illustrated. Although movements are usually repeated on both sides of the body, the illustrations often depict only one side.

The drawings will help you learn the correct postures and movements, and give you a visual sense of the atmosphere or "flavor" of the exercises. In order to do them correctly, you will need to refer to the written instructions. Once you have become familiar with a particular exercise, the illustrations alone may serve as a sufficient reminder.

Set A: Introductory Exercises

Here are instructions for four Self-Breema exercises that are relatively simple and short, yet very nurturing to the body. The exercises were selected to present a range of basic postures, movements, and holds. The instructions for each exercise are preceded by brief general comments on the nature and potential effects of each exercise. Instructions are followed by illustrations of selected movements and postures from the exercise.

Grinding the Wheat

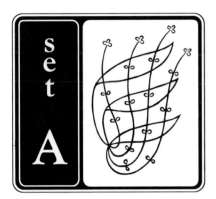

WHEN WHEAT IS TAKEN TO THE MILL TO BE GROUND INTO FLOUR, it is transformed from a coarse substance into something more refined. The flour can then be used to create food to nourish the body and sustain life.

In this exercise, your body moves like a mill stone. Energy blockages in the sacrum and pelvic area are broken up and that energy is made available to the whole body. Grinding the Wheat is an excellent exercise for everyone, as it relieves tension in the lower back and hips, and can safely be done by people with almost any kind of back trouble. It brings energy down from the head to the hara area, and so helps create a more balanced state.

Grinding the Wheat

- Stand comfortably with your feet shoulder-width apart.

- Clasp the forearms behind your back. (1)

- Rotate the hips clockwise in as large a circle as is comfortable. The upper body moves only slightly compared to the hips. (2, 3, 4)

- Continue rotating for at least three breaths, then rotate counterclockwise for at least three breaths.

- Stop rotating and brush from the kidneys down the backs of the legs to the toes. (5, 6, 7) As you straighten up, the hands stay in light contact with the front of the legs and hara until they are back on the kidneys. (8)

- Brush twice more in this fashion.

- Brush from the hara down the front of the legs to the toes. (9, 10) As you straighten, again keep the hands in light contact with the legs.

- Brush twice more. The third time you reach the toes, brush up the front of the legs to the hara. At the hara, the hands come back to back (fingers pointing down) and brush up the midline of the body to overhead, then slowly open out and down to the sides. (11, 12, 13)

- Stand comfortably. (14)

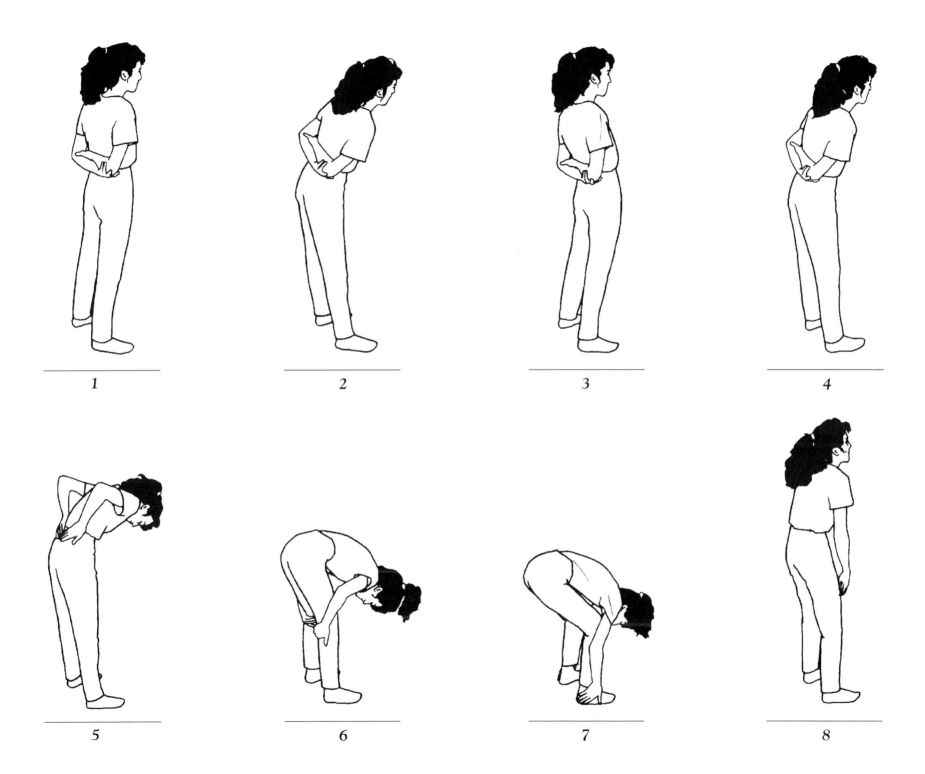

1

2

3

4

5

6

7

8

<u>Grinding the Wheat</u>

73

Continued ⟶

- *Brush from the hara down the front of the legs to the toes. (9, 10) As you straighten, again keep the hands in light contact with the legs.*

- *Brush twice more. The third time you reach the toes, brush up the front of the legs to the hara. At the hara, the hands come back to back (fingers pointing down) and brush up the midline of the body to overhead, then slowly open out and down to the sides. (11, 12, 13)*

- *Stand comfortably. (14)*

9

10

11

12

13

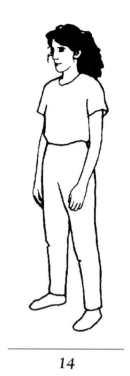

14

Circling the Knee

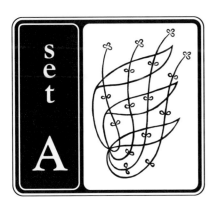

MOST OF US USUALLY TAKE OUR KNEES FOR GRANTED UNTIL ONE IS INJURED, OFTEN THROUGH an accumulation of the stresses that occur daily without our cognizance. Walking or jogging on paved surfaces transmits harsh vibrations to the knee. Prolonged sitting in chairs, driving, and other forms of unnatural leg activity or inactivity can make the knees weak or inflexible, and set them up for injury. Few things are as beneficial for the knees as daily walking on unpaved surfaces, yet many of us don't experience such a surface for days on end.

The knee joint unites four bones, the femur (thigh bone), tibia and fibula (large and small leg bones), and the patella (knee cap). Cartilage, special joint fluid, and confining ligaments complete the joint.

The knee is influenced by many muscles of the thigh and leg, as well as by the articulation of the foot, ankle, hip, and pelvis. A problem with any of these body parts can cause trouble for the knee. Strengthening the thigh muscles is one of the easiest remedies and preventive measures for knee traumas.

Internally, the knee is connected by the meridian system with the kidneys and adrenal glands, especially, and also with the spleen, liver, gall bladder, bladder, and stomach. When the knee hurts or is malfunctioning, it is wise to avoid foods that weaken the kidneys and adrenals, such as salt, sugar, coffee, chocolate, and alcohol.

Circling the Knee is an excellent exercise for the knees. It nurtures the knees directly, bringing them warmth and security. It stretches the supporting muscles and ligaments gradually so they can come into proper balance. It can balance all the meridians of the legs. It gently stimulates the kidneys and adrenals, and so is good to do when feeling tired or stressed. Finally, circling of the torso during this exercise stimulates the digestive organs and provides light stretches for the low back and hips. Thus, it both complements and reinforces the effects of the other exercises in this introductory set.

Circling the Knee

- Sit comfortably in cross-legged position. (1)

- Extend the right leg in front of you, placing the back of the knee on the instep of the left foot. The right hand holds on top of the knee, the left hand holds the underside of the knee. (2)

- Circle the body clockwise in a full but comfortable circle for three breaths. (3, 4, 5)

- Without pause, circle counterclockwise for three breaths. The circling movement originates in the hara.

- Bring the circling to a stop.

- Leaning forward, brush the right hand from the top of the knee down the shin and off the toes, three times. (5, 6, 7)

- Bring the right hand back to the knee and brush with the left hand from under the knee down the inside of the calf and off the toes, three times. (8)

- Bring the right leg in and extend the left leg, resting the left knee on the right instep, and sandwiching it with the left hand on top, and the right hand underneath.

- Repeat the preceding movements, this time circling the body first counterclockwise, then clockwise.

- After brushing the left leg, bring the feet sole-to-sole and hold the toes with your hands one on top of the other, with the big and second toes exposed. (9)

- As you inhale, lean the body back, then look up, stretching the spine. (10) As you exhale, release the stretch, allowing the body to bend forward over the toes. (11) Repeat the stretch and release twice more.

- Bring the hands to the hara, and brush from the hara down the insides of the legs to the toes and off, three times. (12, 13, 14) Brush from the kidneys down the outside of the legs to the toes and off, three times. (15, 16, 17)

- Bring the feet one at a time to cross-legged position and brush the hands to the knees. (18)

- Sit comfortably.

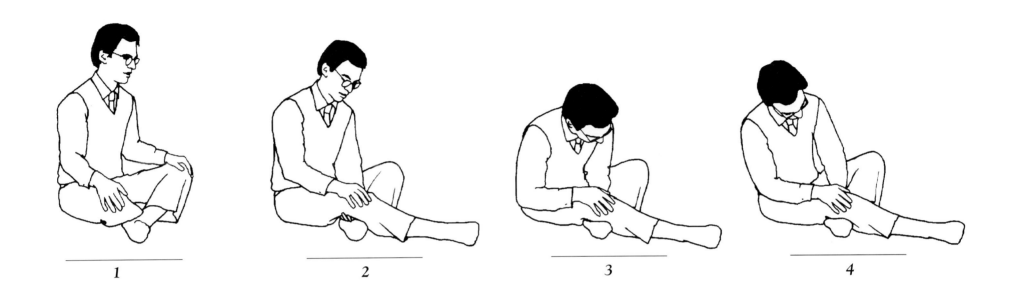

1 2 3 4

5 6 7 8

Circling the Knee

79

Continued ⟶

- *After brushing the left leg, bring the feet sole-to-sole and hold the toes with your hands one on top of the other, with the big and second toes exposed. (9)*

- *As you inhale, lean the body back, then look up, stretching the spine. (10) As you exhale, release the stretch, allowing the body to bend forward over the toes. (11) Repeat the stretch and release twice more.*

- *Bring the hands to the hara, and brush from the hara down the insides of the legs to the toes and off, three times. (12, 13, 14) Brush from the kidneys down the outside of the legs to the toes and off, three times. (15, 16, 17)*

- *Bring the feet one at a time to cross-legged position and brush the hands to the knees. (18)*

- *Sit comfortably.*

9

10

15

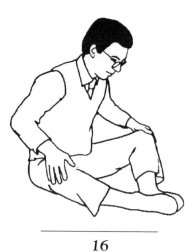

16

11

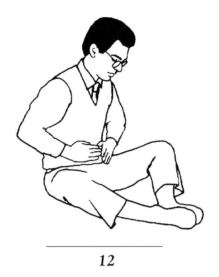

12

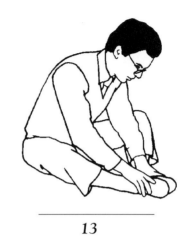

13

14

17

18

Touching the Source

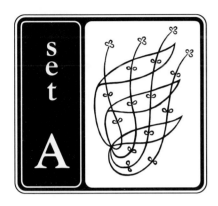

THE SARKHANEH ARE KNOWN AS THE "SOURCE of a thousand oceans." (See page 43.) Here, by striking the sarkhaneh, we may begin to experience the ocean of energy that could be available to us at any given moment. Through the even pace and simple movements of this exercise, we can experience a calming and balancing effect on the emotions.

Touching the Source

- Sit comfortably in seiza position, hands resting on the thighs.

- Strike the left sarkhaneh with the right heel of the hand (the little finger and thumb are connected). (1, 2)

- Brush slowly across the chest as the palm opens, and down the side of the torso to the knee. (3) Repeat, using the left hand, and continue, alternating hands for a total of three times to each side. (4)

- Brush from the knees toward the hara with the palms. At the hara, the hands come back to back, brushing up the midline to overhead, and then opening the arms out and down to the knees. (5, 6, 7, 8)

- Repeat, brushing from the hara twice more.

- End by sitting in seiza position, hands resting comfortably on the thighs.

1   2   3   4

5   6   7   8

Gushing Spring

NO OTHER NAME WOULD SO APTLY DESCRIBE THIS EXERCISE.

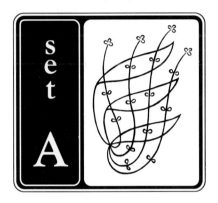

The energy of the heart is like a gushing spring, alive and joyful, playfully expressing its abundance. Gushing Spring can help make that energy available to you, so you feel refreshed, energized, and emotionally balanced. Physically, the exercise stimulates the lung and chest area by deep breathing and free movement of the arms, relieving neck or shoulder tension. It also stimulates the thymus gland and the lymphatic system, which play important roles in resistance to disease.

The joyfulness and simplicity of this exercise make it an excellent choice when you feel worried, afraid, or drained: for example, after an accident or shock to the body, or after a nightmare or other frightening experience. When the mind is calm, the body is experienced as strong. When fear arises, the calmness is lost and the body is weakened, through draining of adrenalin. Gushing Spring can stop this drainage and allow the body to return to a balanced, strong condition.

Gushing Spring

INSTRUCTIONS

- Stand comfortably.

- Bring the fingers and thumb of each hand into loose clusters. (1)

- On inhalation, hop from foot to foot while alternately tapping the sternum gently at heart level with clustered fingertips. (2, 3)

- On exhalation, while continuing the hopping, fling the arms straight up the midline of the body to overhead. Then allow the arms to open out and down to the sides. (4)

- Repeat the tapping and opening of the arms many times.

- Place the hands over the heart, left on top of right, while slowing bringing the hopping to a stop. Hold for three breaths. (5, 6)

- Brush the hands to the sides and stand comfortably. (7, 8)

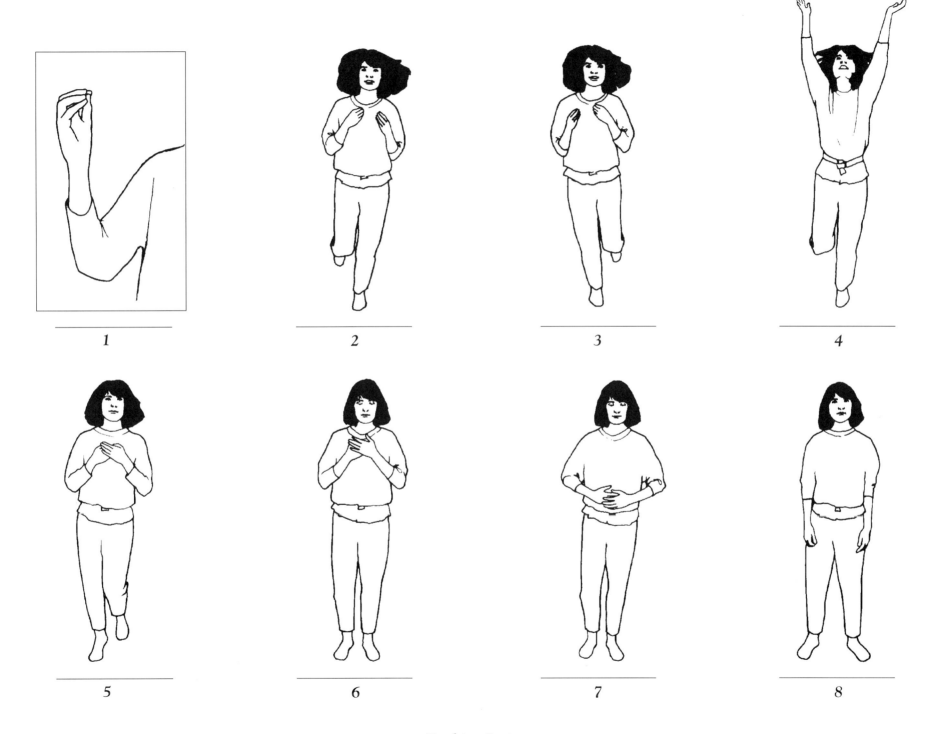

1 2 3 4

5 6 7 8

Chasing the Arrow

THIS EXERCISE IS PURE FUN! BY GETTING YOUR MIND INTERESTED IN

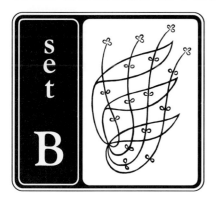

the movements of the body, Chasing the Arrow creates an opening for the joyful participation of the feelings as well. Then you can do the exercise with the full participation of body, mind and feelings. This is a rare experience that can create instant vitality and promote physical, mental, and emotional health.

Chasing the Arrow also improves physical coordination. Kids, and the child-like part of us all, will especially love this exercise.

Chasing the Arrow

INSTRUCTIONS

- Start by standing normally. (1)

- On exhalation, step forward emphatically with the left foot. (2)

- As you inhale, bring the fisted right hand behind the neck (taking an arrow from the quiver) as the left arm extends in front of you with hand fisted (holding the bow). Both feet are flat on the floor, and your body is turned slightly to the right as the head faces forward. (3)

- On exhalation, bring the fisted right hand forward to meet the left hand (placing an arrow in the drawstring). (4)

- On inhalation, draw the right hand back to the earlobe (stretching the drawstring). (5)

- On exhalation, leap forward as you bring your open palms together with arms fully extended in front of you (shooting the arrow). (6)

- After you land, bring your palms to the kidneys. (7) Then hop backwards from foot to foot to your original starting place. (8)

- Keeping your palms on the kidneys, jump up and land with the left foot forward.

- Repeat the whole sequence twice more.

- After hopping back to your starting place for the third time, inhale as you raise both hands up at the same time (palms facing each other but not touching) over the right shoulder (removing the quiver). (9)

- Bend forward slowly as you exhale, bringing your hands near the floor (placing the quiver on the ground), palms facing up. (10)

- Slowly stand upright, allowing the arms to return to your sides. (11)

- Stand normally and experience your body.

1

2

3

4

5

6

7

8

Continued $\longrightarrow$

- *After hopping back to your starting place for the third time, inhale as you raise both hands up at the same time (palms facing each other but not touching) over the right shoulder (removing the quiver). (9)*

- *Bend forward slowly as you exhale, bringing your hands near the floor (placing the quiver on the ground), palms facing up. (10)*

- *Slowly stand upright, allowing the arms to return to your sides. (11)*

- *Stand normally and experience your body.*

9

10

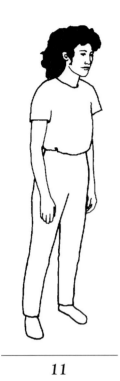

11

Harvesting the Resin

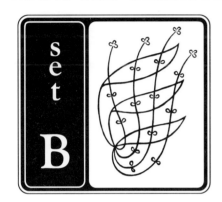

MANY SELF-BREEMA EXERCISES TAKE EXCESS ENERGY FROM THE MIND and distribute it to the lower body. Harvesting the Resin helps to "spread the energy around." As you lean down the legs, you are balancing both the three yin meridians on the inside of the legs (spleen, liver, and kidney), and the yang meridians on the outside of the legs (stomach, gall bladder, bladder). These organs get a double workout; in addition to being stimulated via the meridians, the rhythmic bending forward and then straightening of your torso gently compresses and then releases them. This energizes them, and helps their blood circulation.

Harvesting the Resin can increase flexibility of the low back and hips. "Harvest the Resin" shortly before mealtime to stimulate your digestive organs. It is helpful for digestive and circulatory conditions.

Harvesting the Resin

- Begin by sitting cross-legged. (1)

- Fold the right leg back so that the foot is near the buttock, and the knee and instep are resting on the floor. (2)

- Bring both hands to the tops of the thighs (fingertips toward the insides of the thighs). Lean forward gradually, and as you do, let the hands lean into the thighs. (3) Hold briefly, then gradually release as you straighten up.

- Move the hands about a hand's-width down the thighs, and again lean, hold, and release.

- Continue down the thighs, and then down the calves to the toes. Each time you lean in, the hands transmit only as much weight to the thighs or legs as they receive naturally from the movement of your body leaning forward. No pressing or muscular force is present. (4, 5, 6, 7)

- Bring both hands to the hara, and brush them down the thighs and legs to the toes and off, three times. (8, 9, 10)

- Maintaining the rhythm of the exercise, switch the leg positions so your left leg is folded back, and your right leg is in front of you.

- Repeat the lean, hold, release down the thighs and legs, and brush three times.

- Return to sitting in cross-legged position, hands resting on your knees. (11)

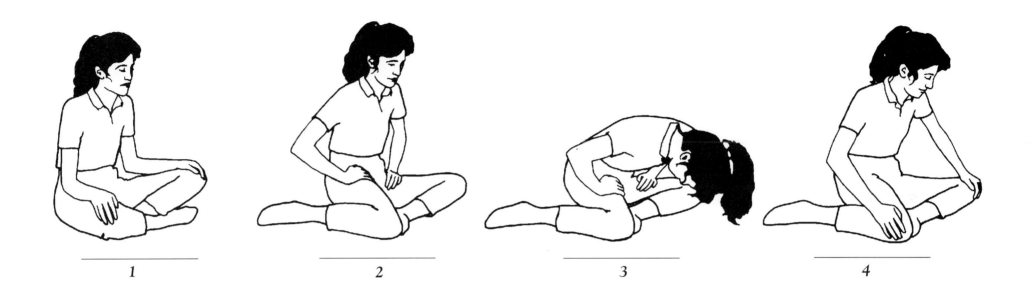

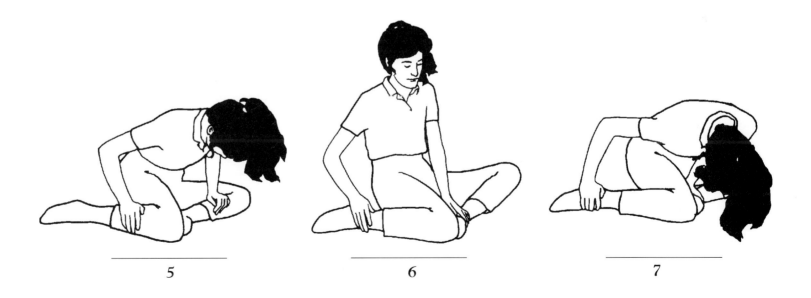

- *Bring both hands to the hara, and brush them down the thighs and legs to the toes and off, three times. (8, 9, 10)*

- *Maintaining the rhythm of the exercise, switch the leg positions so your left leg is folded back, and your right leg is in front of you.*

- *Repeat the lean, hold, release down the thighs and legs, and brush three times.*

- *Return to sitting in cross-legged position, hands resting on your knees. (11)*

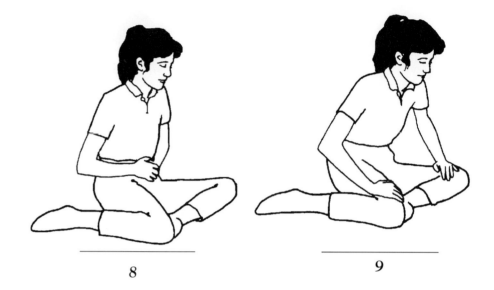

8   9

10

11

Touching the Mountain

HOW STRONGLY NINE BREATHS CAN AFFECT YOUR BODY'S ENERGY!

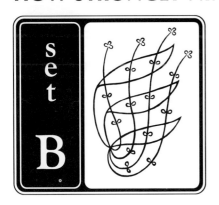

Just a few simple postures and a few quiet breaths. It's as if someone whispered you a profound secret: through your breathing, you can become connected to your own body, and to Life. Calmness and serenity follow naturally.

Touching the Mountain

INSTRUCTIONS

- Stand comfortably with your heels together.

- Place your left hand on the hara, and your right hand on top of the left. (1)

- Hold for three full breaths. (2)

- Slide the hands up to the chest at heart level, and hold for three breaths.

- Slide the hands up to the top of the chest and close to (but not quite touching) the face, bringing the palms to cover the eyes (they close as they are covered). The fingers are relaxed and resting on the forehead. (3)

- Hold for three breaths.

- Brush up the forehead, over the crown of the head, down the back of the head and neck, and down the chest and torso, letting the hands come to rest at your sides. (4, 5, 6)

- Stand comfortably.

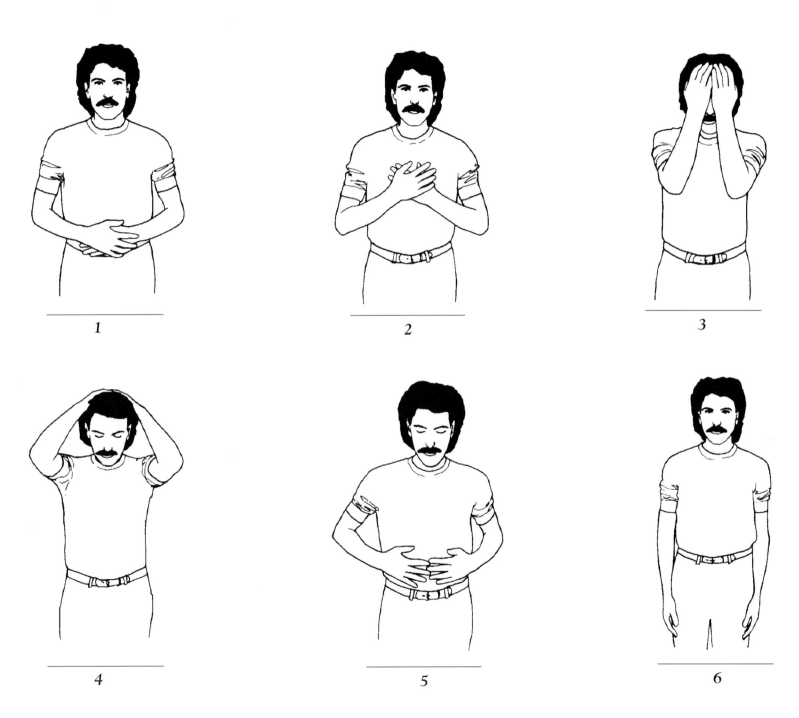

1

2

3

4

5

6

Hulling the Walnut

HULLING THE WALNUT HELPS YOUR BODY COME OUT OF THE SHELL

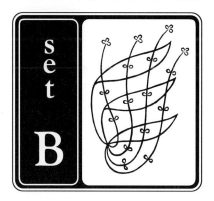

that tension creates. Get rid of the brittle and the bitter, and let the inner vitality come out! Wonderful for tight, inflexible hips and pelvis, and for tight thigh and lower back muscles. Excellent for the digestive system, both because of its direct stimulation of blood circulation to digestive organs, and because it works on the stomach, spleen, liver, and gall bladder meridians.

Hulling the Walnut

- Sit comfortably in seiza position. (1)

- Circle the hands on the hips, from the sacrum and tailbone to the hip sockets. Both hands move at the same time, but while one hand brushes forward to the hip socket, the other hand brushes back towards the sacrum. (2, 3)

- As you brush, the body naturally rocks gently from side to side.

- Continue for three breaths.

- Lean from the top of the thighs down to the knees, using the soft inner part of the forearms. Lean alternately, with left forearm, right, left, etc. (4, 5, 6)

- Make the hands into loose fists and bring them to the inner part of the top of the thighs. The wrists are crossed, so the right fist contacts the left thigh, and vice versa. (7)

- While leaning the body forward and back in a gentle semi-circular movement, lean the flat part of the fists alternately down the inner thighs to the knees. (8, 9, 10)

- Bring the hands to the top of the thighs (fingertips oriented towards the midline). (11)

- Lean the palms and hands alternately into the thighs as they travel down to the knees. (Continue the semi-circular, back-and-forth leaning with your body.) (12, 13, 14)

- Circle the hands on the knees for three breaths (both hands circling at the same time). (15, 16)

- Bring the hands to the kidneys and brush from the kidneys down the thighs and legs to the feet and back to the kidneys, in a continuous movement, three times. (17, 18, 19)

- In the same continuous movement, brush the hands down the thighs and let them rest on the knees. (20)

- Sit and experience your body sitting.

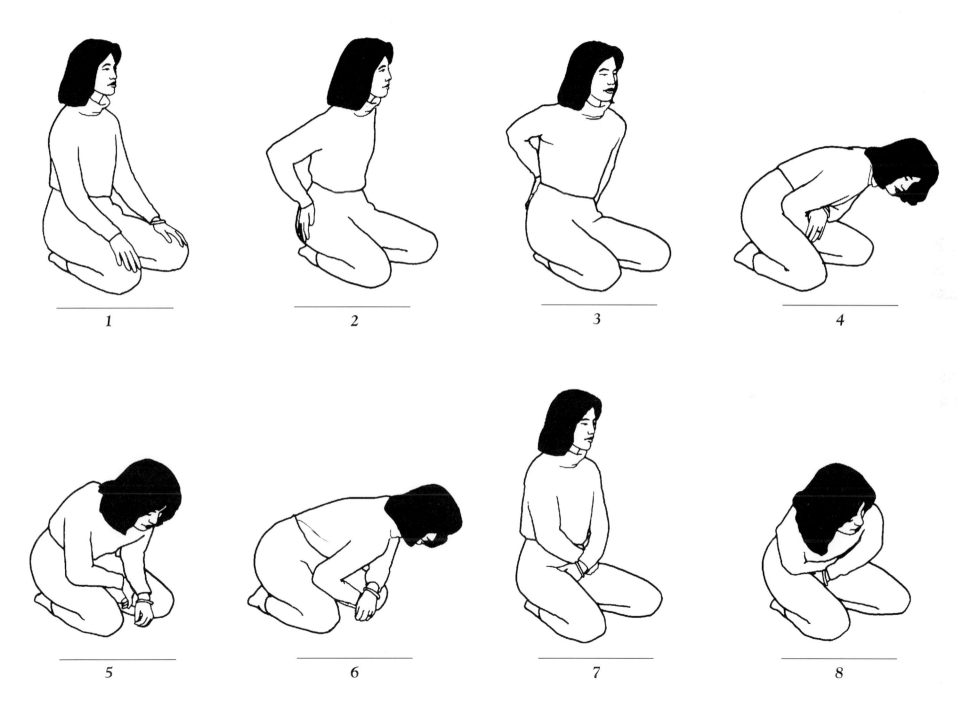

1

2

3

4

5

6

7

8

Continued ⟶

- *While leaning the body forward and back in a gentle semi-circular movement, lean the flat part of the fists alternately down the inner thighs to the knees. (8, 9, 10)*

- *Bring the hands to the top of the thighs (fingertips oriented towards the midline). (11)*

- *Lean the palms and hands alternately into the thighs as they travel down to the knees. (Continue the semi-circular, back-and-forth leaning with your body.) (12, 13, 14)*

- *Circle the hands on the knees for three breaths (both hands circling at the same time). (15, 16)*

- *Bring the hands to the kidneys and brush from the kidneys down the thighs and legs to the feet and back to the kidneys, in a continuous movement, three times. (17, 18, 19)*

- *In the same continuous movement, brush the hands down the thighs and let them rest on the knees. (20)*

- *Sit and experience your body sitting.*

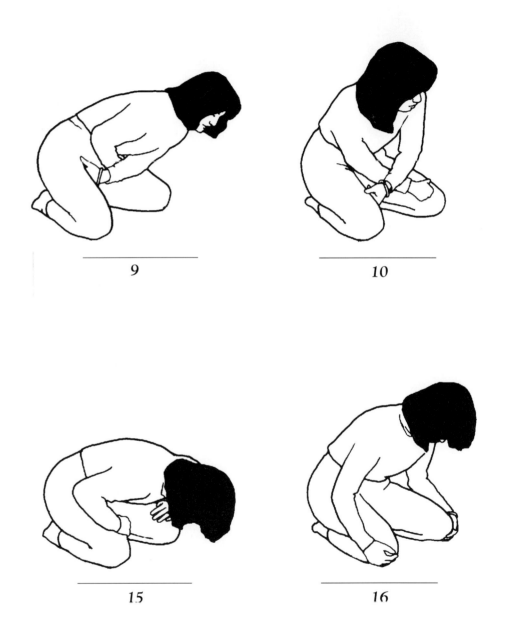

9   10

15   16

Evening Posture

IF YOUR NECK HURTS, YOU MAY FALL IN LOVE WITH THIS EXERCISE.

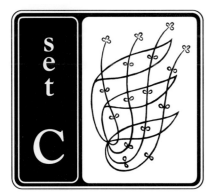

Do it and then ask yourself, "What happened to all that tension?" Tight neck and shoulder muscles are influenced by these gentle stretches to find a new state of balance: one more free of tension. Alertness to breathing and a view of the entire body while inhaling and exhaling can put you in contact with your supporting energy, which has healing qualities.

Evening Posture

- Stand comfortably.

- Make the hands into very loose fists.

- Place the right fist into the left armpit, and the left fist into the right armpit. (1)

- As you inhale, slowly raise the elbows towards the ceiling and stretch your head back. (2)

- As you exhale, slowly lower the elbows and your head. Let both the head and elbows relax fully. (3)

- Repeat the stretching and lowering two more times.

- Open your hands, keeping them under the armpits for one breath. (4)

- Brush the hands over the chest as the forearms uncross, to your sides. (5, 6, 7)

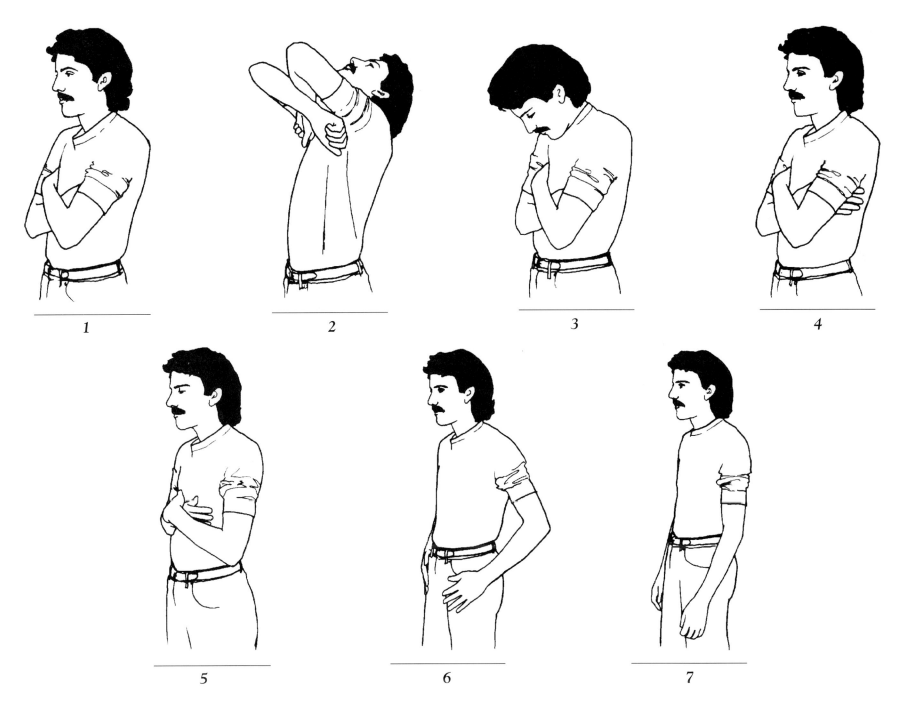

1

2

3

4

5

6

7

Dancing On the Grapes

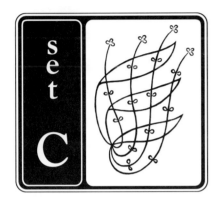

THIS SIMPLE EXERCISE IS VERY BENEFICIAL FOR THE BACK. ONE OF its primary movements is gentle twisting, which is helpful in aligning the spine. The hands rest on the "kidney area," the part of the back that can directly influence the kidneys and adrenal glands. The movements of the exercise first nurture, then stimulate the kidneys and adrenals, which perform so many essential functions in the body and which are responsible for the body's energy reserves.

This exercise is especially good for anyone recovering from a low back injury, or anyone with a stiff neck. It gently gets the circulation going, too.

Dancing On the Grapes

- Stand comfortably, with the feet shoulder-width apart. Place your palms on the kidneys. (1)

- Inhale and twist to the left, gently stretching your body and leaning into the left kidney; allow your feet to pivot. As the stretch comes to completion, stretch upwards, creating a stretch up the spine. (2)

- As you exhale, come back to center (your starting position), then inhale and repeat, now stretching to the right. The movement is without pause. (3, 4)

- Continue alternately stretching to each side, three times to each side altogether, then face straight ahead.

- Keeping the hands on the kidneys, hop gently from foot to foot for three breaths. The shoulders, arms, and whole body are loose and relaxed. (5, 6)

- Bring the hopping to a gradual stop, then brush from the kidneys down the back of the thighs and legs to the toes and off, three times. (7, 8)

- Brush from the hara down the front of the thighs and legs to the toes and off, three times. (9, 10, 11) On the third and final brush, brush back up the front of the legs, up the midline of the body (hands come back to back) to overhead, opening the arms out and down to your sides. (12-17)

- Stand comfortably.

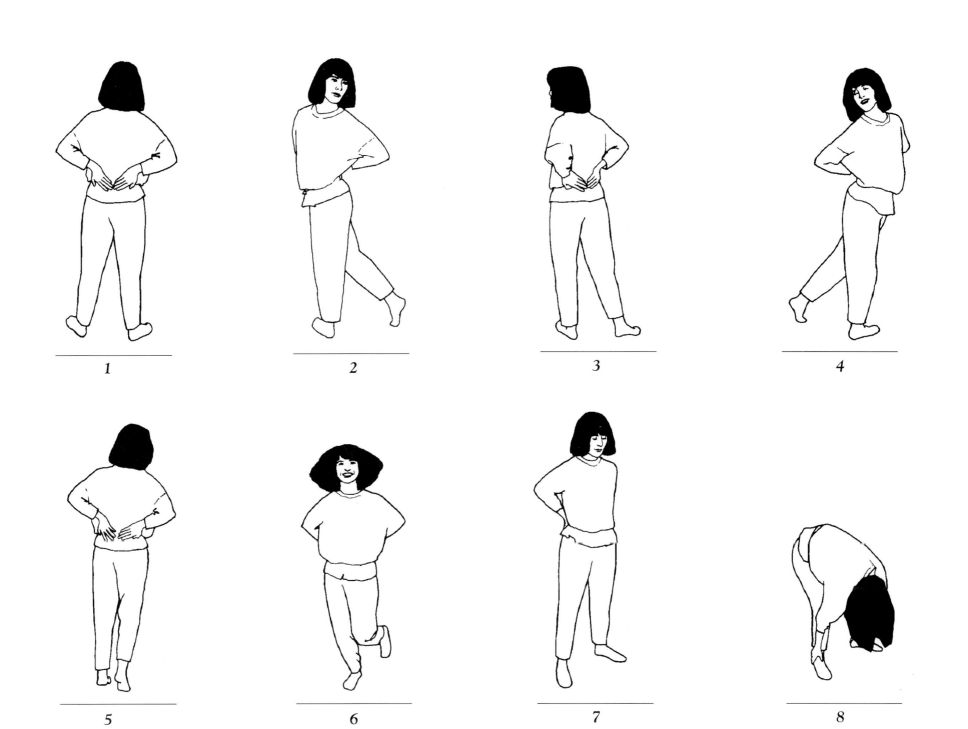

1

2

3

4

5

6

7

8

Continued ⟶

- *Brush from the hara down the front of the thighs and legs to the toes and off, three times. (9, 10, 11) On the third and final brush, brush back up the front of the legs, up the midline of the body (hands come back to back) to overhead, opening the arms out and down to your sides. (12-17)*

- *Stand comfortably.*

9

10

11

16

12

13

14

15

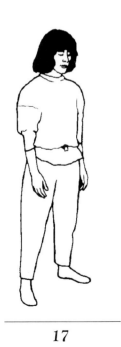

17

Erasing the Page

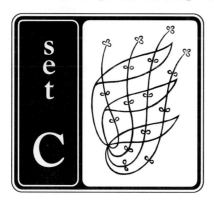

ANYONE WHO HAS LEARNED THIS EXERCISE WILL ATTEST TO THE surprising effects these few simple movements can have. They release tension in the facial muscles and eyes, and through them, help relax the whole body. Mental tension is released, too, leaving the mind relaxed, clear, and available.

Erasing the Page stimulates points on the stomach, gall bladder, small intestine, and large intestine meridians, and is very effective for promoting sinus drainage.

Erasing the Page

- Sit or stand comfortably, and bring the hands to palm the eyes. (1) Brush over the crown (the top of the head), down the back of the head, and off the chin. (2, 3)

- Bring the hands edge to edge to palm the eyebrows and the forehead. (4) Brush to the ears and off the chin. (5)

- Place the fingertips at the top of the nose, with the whole hand in contact with the face. (6) Brush, emphasizing the middle fingers, from the sides of the nose down to the cheekbones, then along the cheekbones to the jaw and down the jaw and off the chin. (7)

- Bring the thumb and little finger of each hand close together and brush with the round fleshy part between the thumb and wrist from the sides of the nose, under the cheekbones to the ears, to the back of the head (one hand comes on top of the other) and down the neck and jaw and off the chin. (8, 9, 10)

- Palm the eyebrows and brush three times over the crown and down the neck and jaw and off the chin. (11, 12)

- Brush from the closed eyes down the face along the cheekbones to the jaw and off the chin, three times. (Rest the middle fingers on each eyelid to do this brush.) (13, 14)

- If you're sitting, bring the hands to rest on the knees; if standing, they come to the sides. (15)

1   2   3

4   5   6

Continued ⟶

- *Place the fingertips at the top of the nose, with the whole hand in contact with the face. (6) Brush, emphasizing the middle fingers, from the sides of the nose down to the cheekbones, then along the cheekbones to the jaw and down the jaw and off the chin. (7)*

- *Bring the thumb and little finger of each hand close together and brush with the round fleshy part between the thumb and wrist from the sides of the nose, under the cheekbones to the ears, to the back of the head (one hand comes on top of the other) and down the neck and jaw and off the chin. (8, 9, 10)*

- *Palm the eyebrows and brush three times over the crown and down the neck and jaw and off the chin. (11, 12)*

- *Brush from the closed eyes down the face along the cheekbones to the jaw and off the chin, three times. (Rest the middle fingers on each eyelid to do this brush.) (13, 14)*

- *If you're sitting, bring the hands to rest on the knees; if standing, they come to the sides. (15)*

7

8

12

13

9

10

11

14

15

Opening the Heart

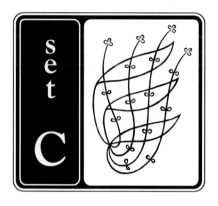

THIS IS A SHORT EXERCISE THAT HELPS RELEASE TENSION between the shoulder blades, and in the shoulder joints and arms. It also opens the chest, stretching chest muscles, which, when tight, restrict breathing. The result is a feeling of lightness in the chest and upper body, as if a weight were lifted from one's shoulders.

Opening the Heart

- Stand comfortably.

- Bring the palms together, interlacing the fingers. Your thumbs are pointing straight in front of you. (1)

- As you inhale, stretch the arms in front of you, creating a stretch in the shoulders and between the scapulae. (2) When the arms are extended, turn the hands so that the palms open out. The backs of the hands are visible to your eyes, creating an extra stretch in the wrists and knuckles. This movement is done continuously as soon as the arms are extended. (3)

- As you exhale, bring the hands to your chest (palms face toward the ceiling). Lower the elbows and create a stretch in the knuckles (the fingers stay interlaced). The chest is opened and the head is extended back. (4)

- Repeat these movements as you inhale and exhale twice more.

- After the third exhalation, turn the hands in toward you, so palms touch the chest at heart level, and brush the hands down the chest to your hara, around to the kidneys, down the back of the legs to the toes, up the front of the legs to the hara, and then fling hands out and up in front of you to overhead, opening out and down until the arms come to rest at the sides. (5-9)

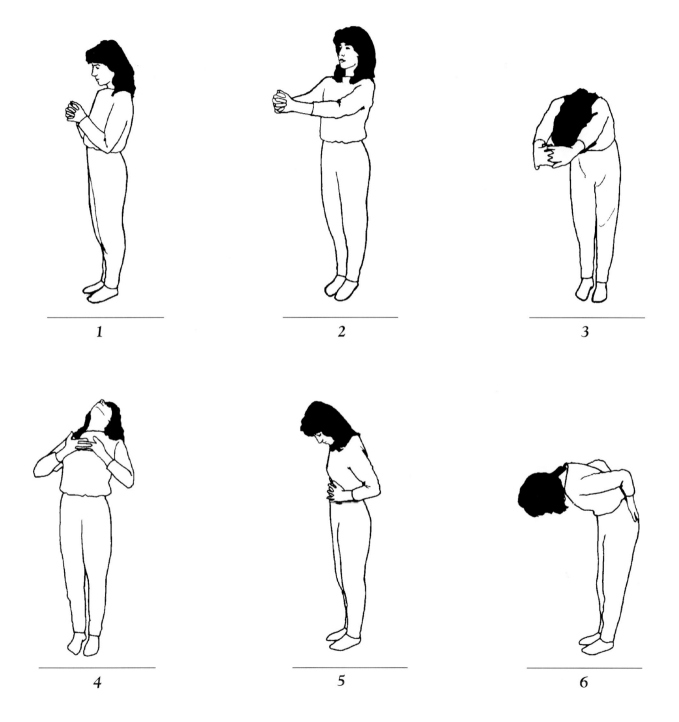

1

2

3

4

5

6

Continued ⟶

■ *After the third exhalation,*
turn the hands in toward you,
so palms touch the chest at
heart level, and brush the
hands down the chest to your
hara, around to the kidneys,
down the back of the legs to
the toes, up the front of the
legs to the hara, and then fling
hands out and up in front of
you to overhead, opening out
and down until the arms come
to rest at the sides. (5-9)

7

8

9

Creating Flow

THIS IS ONE OF THE SIMPLEST AND BEST EXERCISES FOR RELEASING

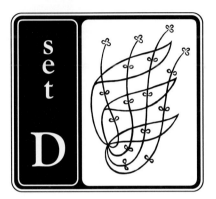

tension in the neck. It can be a great aid for anyone who works at a desk or drives or does other work that taxes the eyes.

Tight neck muscles impede the proper flow of blood and energy to the head, and from the head to the rest of the body. This exercise helps to normalize that flow, bringing balance and smooth function.

Creating Flow

- Sit in cross-legged position. (1)

- Bring the right leg up and rest the sole of the foot on top of the left foot, along the instep and inside surface.

- Rest your left hand on the right knee, and the right hand on the left wrist, so the hands and forearms wrap around the knee. (2)

- Be sure you're totally comfortable, and let your head hang forward. (3)

- Slowly rotate your head counterclockwise, in a loose circle. Whenever you come to a place where you feel tension, stop and hold that position for one full breath, then continue. (4, 5, 6)

- When you've come full circle, again rotate the head counterclockwise (but without stopping), choosing a definite speed with your mind.

- Rotate the head a third time, allowing your body to choose the speed.

- Brush with both hands from the knee down the leg and off the toes, one time. (7, 8)

- Switch the position of your legs so the right leg is down and the left is up.

- Repeat the entire sequence, this time rotating your head clockwise.

- Bring both feet next to each other with the soles flat on the floor and your knees up.

- Wrap your arms around your knees and clasp one wrist with the other hand. (9)

- Rotate your head counterclockwise three times, allowing one full breath for each rotation. On inhalation, the head moves from chin towards the chest to head hanging back, chin up. (10) On exhalation, the second half of the rotation is completed and the chin again comes towards the chest. (11)

- Then rotate your head clockwise three times.

- Brush the hands from your knees down the legs to the toes and off, one time. (12, 13)

- Sit in cross-legged position, resting the hands on the knees. (14)

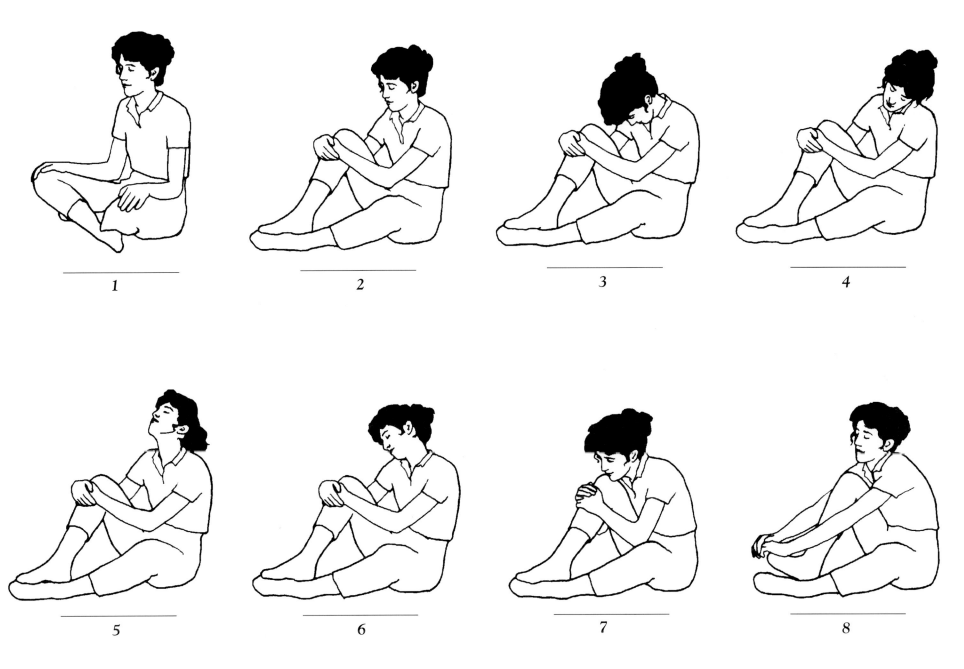

1

2

3

4

5

6

7

8

- Bring both feet next to each other with the soles flat on the floor and your knees up.

- Wrap your arms around your knees and clasp one wrist with the other hand. (9)

- Rotate your head counterclockwise three times, allowing one full breath for each rotation. On inhalation, the head moves from chin towards the chest to head hanging back, chin up. (10) On exhalation, the second half of the rotation is completed and the chin again comes towards the chest. (11)

- Then rotate your head clockwise three times.

- Brush the hands from your knees down the legs to the toes and off, one time. (12, 13)

- Sit in cross-legged position, resting the hands on the knees. (14)

9

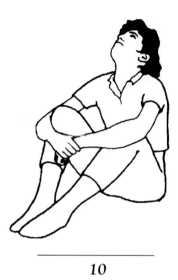

10

11

12

13

14

Fire Posture

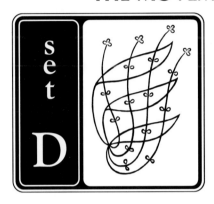

THE MOVEMENTS OF THIS EXERCISE SUGGEST THE BEHAVIOR

of a flame: shooting up suddenly, quickly spreading, then dying down. They also suggest the apparent course of the sun at sunrise, midday, and sunset.

When fire flames up from the earth, it spreads light and clarity. The definite movements of Fire Posture can help create clarity within you, through the attention and coordination that they require.

Fire Posture

INSTRUCTIONS

- Stand comfortably with feet shoulder-width apart.(1)

- In a swift, sudden, and definite movement as you exhale, swing the arms up in front of you to 45 degrees above horizontal. The arms are body-width apart, the palms face each other, and the hands are fully open. (2)

- Hold this position for three breaths.

- With the next exhalation, open the arms out to your sides, 45 degrees above horizontal. Palms now face forward. At the same time, step your feet apart to twice shoulder-width. This movement is also quick and definite. (3)

- Hold this position for three breaths.

- With your next exhalation, quickly bring your arms behind your back, with the left hand holding the right wrist. At the same time, step your feet together so the heels touch. Hold this position for three breaths. (4)

- At a normal, comfortable pace, come to standing with feet shoulder-width apart, and brush your left arm from the shoulder to the fingertips and off, three times. (5, 6)

- Brush the right arm three times. (7, 8)

- Bend forward, bringing your cupped hands, touching edge to edge, near the floor between your legs. (9)

- Straighten up, raising your cupped hands up, close in front of the body, until they come above the head. (10, 11)

- In the same continuous movement, turn the hands palms down above the head, as if "pouring" their contents onto your head, and lower the hands to your sides, keeping the palms facing the body, but not quite touching it as you lower them. (12, 13, 14, 15)

- Stand normally.

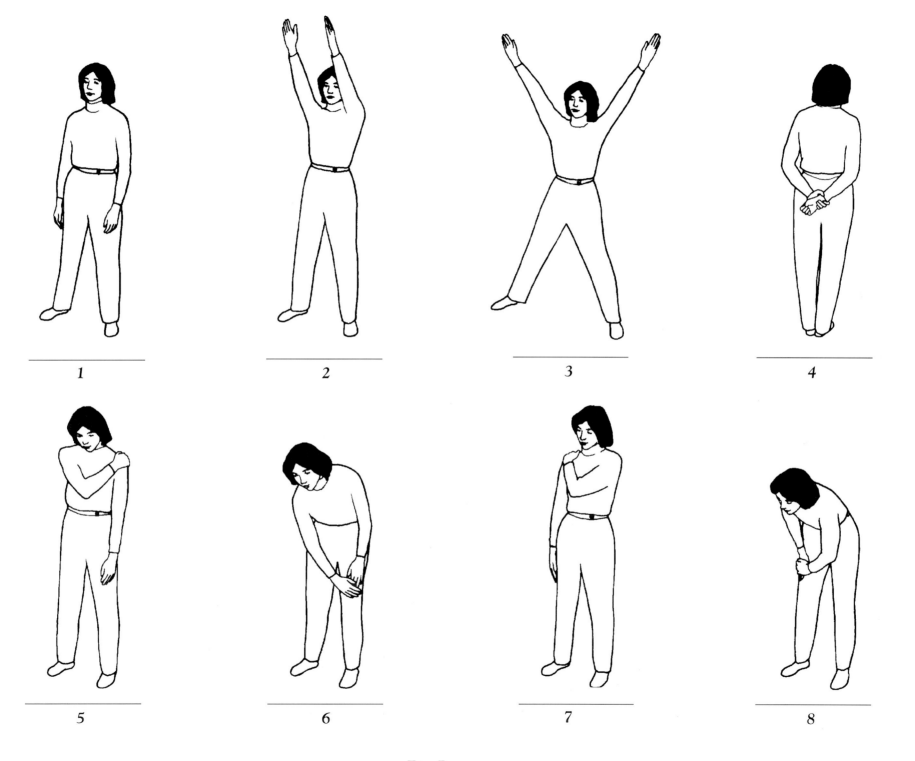

1

2

3

4

5

6

7

8

Continued ⟶

- Bend forward, bringing your cupped hands, touching edge to edge, near the floor between your legs. (9)

- Straighten up, raising your cupped hands up, close in front of the body, until they come above the head. (10, 11)

- In the same continuous movement, turn the hands palms down above the head, as if "pouring" their contents onto your head, and lower the hands to your sides, keeping the palms facing the body, but not quite touching it as you lower them. (12, 13, 14, 15)

- Stand normally.

9

10

11

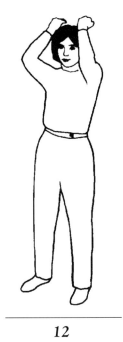

12

13

14

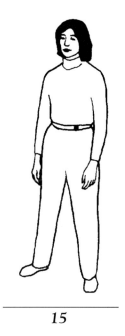

15

Tilling the Soil

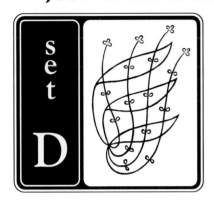

JUST AS THE EARTH NEEDS TO BE WORKED IN ORDER TO BECOME suitable for planting and growing, so must the body in order to remain a suitable home. This exercise is called Tilling the Soil because it can do for the body's energy what plowing does for the land. Plowing takes the surface soil and turns it under while bringing the buried soil up to the surface. Tilling the Soil takes the excess of energy that we all carry in our head and upper body, and brings it down towards the feet, creating a more equal distribution of energy throughout the body.

When your brain feels congested so that you can't think clearly, try this exercise. It lets in light and air, and can bring the calmness and clarity essential for productive mentation. When you are tense, or exhausted from too much mental activity, try this exercise. The fullness of movement, and the rhythmic and simple quality of Tilling the Soil make it a joy for the body. You'll find your heels are hungry for this kind of a beating. Because of its stimulating effect on the kidney meridian, Tilling the Soil is a great revitalizer. It can give your body the fresh supply of energy it needs in a pinch.

Tilling the Soil

- Sit comfortably in cross-legged position, with the hands resting on your knees. (1)

- Bring your legs out in front of you, with your feet touching, sole-to-sole. (2)

- Hold the toes with your left hand.

- Make your right hand into a loose fist. (3)

- Lean back with your whole body, raising the fist. (4)

- Lean the body forward, letting the fist drop on to the inside surface of both heels. (5, 6)

- The heel of the hand and the flat part of the fingers (middle phalanges) form the part of the fist that strikes the heels.

- Continue pounding the heels, choosing a rhythm that is completely comfortable for your body. Remember to use your whole body, and to pound without any tension in the shoulder or arm. No muscular effort is necessary; let the weight and rhythm of the body create a natural force that does the work. When you do this correctly, there is no pain or feeling of being beaten. The body simply accepts the weight of the body, joyfully.

- When you feel you've pounded enough (three or more breaths), brush the hands from the heels down the soles of the feet to the toes, and back up the dorsum (top surface) of the feet, three times. (7, 8, 9, 10)

- Return to sitting cross-legged with your hands on the knees. (11)

1

2

3

4

5

6

Continued ⟶

- *When you feel you've pounded enough (three or more breaths), brush the hands from the heels down the soles of the feet to the toes, and back up the dorsum (top surface) of the feet, three times. (7, 8, 9, 10)*

- *Return to sitting cross-legged with your hands on the knees. (11)*

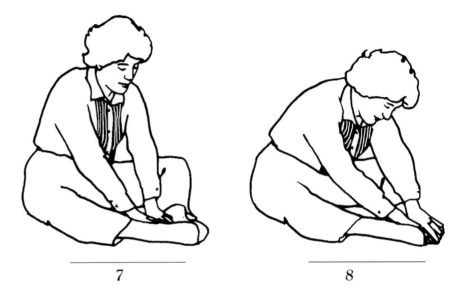

7   8

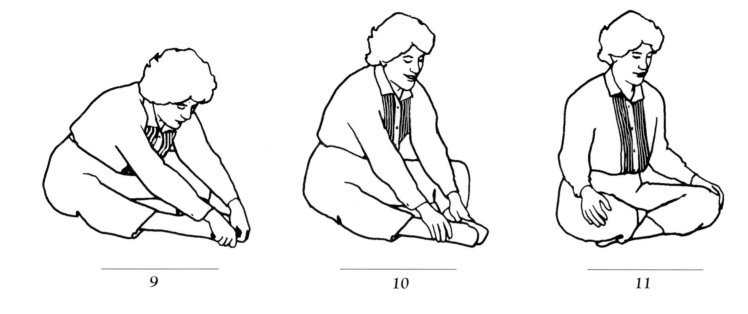

9

10

11

Giving to the Earth

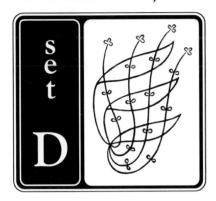

IN BREEMAVA, PEOPLE LIVE WITH THE KNOWLEDGE THAT THE BODY is made out of the physical substances that compose the Earth, and is itself a part of the planet Earth. This knowledge supports the commonsense wisdom that looks to the Earth for help with health and healing. This exercise is so named because it takes excess energy from the mind and brings it down to the Earth (the body), and also because it increases one's connection with the Earth. In effect, it lowers one's center of gravity to the abdominal and pelvic area, lending strength and solidity to one's legs and feet, planting them firmly on the ground.

It is an excellent exercise for low back or hip problems. It strengthens the liver by stretching the Achilles tendons, because they are reciprocally related via the meridian system. It improves balance. You may recognize exercises of similar form as cornerstones of Tai-Chi and other martial and internal arts, which also understand the importance of this type of movement in creating balance and health.

Giving to the Earth

- Stand comfortably with feet shoulder-width apart. (1)

- Bring the hands to hold the kidneys. (2)

- Slowly shift your weight into the right foot, and inhale, raising the left leg (leading with the knee) as high as is comfortable, while raising your face upwards at the same time. (3, 4, 5) Your leg steps out to the side and then slowly lowers to the floor, back to its original spot, as you exhale, and the head lowers. (6, 7)

- Let your weight sink into the left foot, raise the right leg as you inhale, and lower it as you exhale. (8, 9, 10)

- Continue for a total of three times on each side. The entire sequence should be experienced as one smooth, continuous movement.

- Now inhale, rise up onto your toes and arch back gently, looking up. Your hands lean into and support the kidneys. (11)

- Exhale as you come back down onto the soles of the feet, bending the knees slightly and lowering your head. Your weight sinks into the feet. (12)

- Repeat this raising and lowering six more times.

- Brush down the back of your thighs to the knees, then around to the front of the knees and down the front of the legs to the toes and off. (13, 14, 15, 16)

- Cup the hands (they're connected edge to edge) just above floor level and raise them up in front of the body to shoulder height. (17, 18) Cross the hands, placing one over the other on the chest at heart level, and brush down the torso, allowing the hands to come to rest at your sides. This is one smooth, continuous movement, from the moment you begin brushing. (19, 20, 21, 22)

- Stand comfortably.

1

2

3

4

5

6

7

8

Continued ⟶

- *Let your weight sink into the left foot, raise the right leg as you inhale, and lower it as you exhale. (8, 9, 10)*

- *Continue for a total of three times on each side. The entire sequence should be experienced as one smooth, continuous movement.*

- *Now inhale, rise up onto your toes and arch back gently, looking up. Your hands lean into and support the kidneys. (11)*

- *Exhale as you come back down onto the soles of the feet, bending the knees slightly and lowering your head. Your weight sinks into the feet. (12)*

- *Repeat this raising and lowering six more times.*

- *Brush down the back of your thighs to the knees, then around to the front of the knees and down the front of the legs to the toes and off. (13, 14, 15, 16)*

- *Cup the hands (they're connected edge to edge) just above floor level and raise them up in front of the body to shoulder height. (17, 18) Cross the hands, placing one over the other on the chest at heart level, and brush down the torso, allowing the hands to come to rest at your sides. This is one smooth, continuous movement, from the moment you begin brushing. (19, 20, 21, 22)*

- *Stand comfortably.*

9

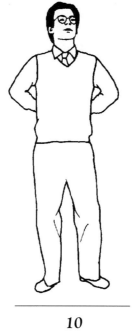

10

11

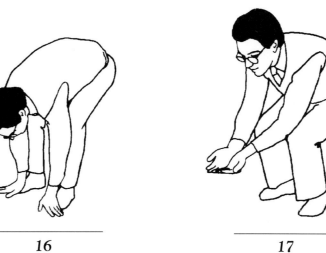

16

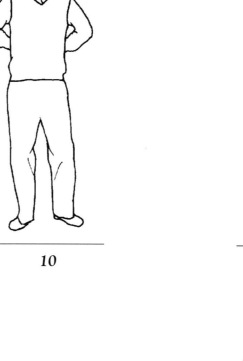

17

18

Giving to the Earth

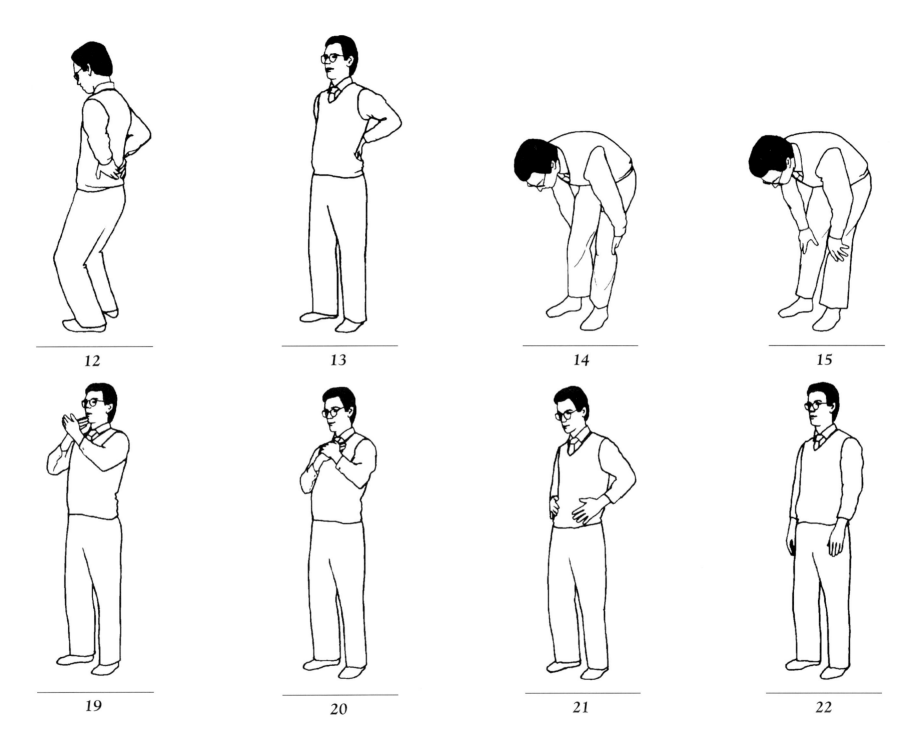

12

13

14

15

19

20

21

22

Closing the Gate

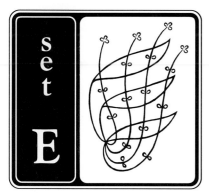

OFFERING A GENTLE STRETCH FOR THE LOW BACK, SHOULDERS, and chest, the smooth and careful movements of Closing the Gate require that the mind remain attentive and clear. The breath becomes slow and unforced, and so exerts an extremely calming and balancing effect on the body and emotions. Finally, we may experience a moment of harmony between the body, mind, and feelings.

The movements of this exercise are similar to those of a large gate, swinging slowly but steadily from an open to a closed position, and then back again. Closing the gate implies order and completion. On returning home, one closes the gate and then enters the house. This means coming to your body and connecting to it by bringing the interest of the mind to the activity of your body. Likewise, one closes the gate to keep that which is precious inside. Here, the precious treasure is the balanced, vital energy which can become available to you.

Closing the Gate

INSTRUCTIONS

This exercise is done in one smooth, continuous motion. Each position is held only long enough to register that you are fully in that posture, then the body continues. There is no actual pause.

- Begin by standing with your heels together. (1)

- Raise your arms out to the sides, until they are 45 degrees above shoulder level, with palms facing forward. (2)

- Slowly move the arms until they're extended in front of the body, with the right palm on top of the left, palms facing down towards the floor. (3, 4)

- Allow the body to bend forward from the waist until the hands come near to the knees, still with the right palm over the left. (5)

- Straighten the body up as you draw the hands upward, with palms facing the body and close to, but not touching, the thighs.

- At hara level, turn the palms up (so now the right palm is under the left), and continue up until the hands are in front of the heart. (6)

- At heart level, the palms turn to face the body, as the arms extend out to the sides, again 45 degress above shoulder level. (7, 8)

- Repeat the entire sequence twice more.

- When the arms come up above shoulder level for the third time, lower them slowly to your sides and stand normally. (9, 10)

1

2

3

4

5

6

7

8

Continued ⟶

■ *When the arms come up above shoulder level for the third time, lower them slowly to your sides and stand normally. (9, 10)*

9

10

Dropping the Load

WHEN YOU GO ON A LONG HIKE, YOU SOON FEEL BURDENED BY ANY SUPERFLUOUS BAGGAGE.

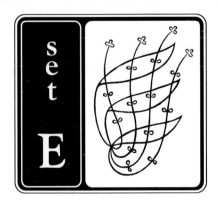

The more you walk, the more willing you are to leave unnecessary items behind. Tension also is experienced as a burden we carry with us. It adds weight to the body, and creates stiffness and eventually pain. The job of the muscles and the skeletal system is to hold the body up and allow it to move. The more tension we carry with us, the more work the body must do to move or maintain posture.

Dropping the Load allows you to let go of that unnecessary tension. It stretches the small ligaments that hold every vertebrae of your spine in place. This decompresses the intervertebral discs, allowing them to absorb water and nutrients necessary for their healthy functioning. When you let go of the stretch, the spine falls back into place and the vertebrae can adjust and align themselves spontaneously. A tremendous amount of tension is released, and energy can flow through the spinal cord and spinal nerves unimpeded. Internal organs can also reposition themselves under the beneficial influence of this exercise.

The sacral ligaments are stretched, too, and by aligning the sacrum, the body gains a sense of solidity and groundedness. Balance and coordination may also increase.

Try Dropping the Load, and breathe a sigh of relief. Enjoy the new experience of your body, freer of tension and more alive.

Dropping the Load

- Come comfortably into this position: soles flat on the floor, palms flat on the floor with your arms extended behind you, and your buttocks just above the floor. (1)

- As you inhale, bring your knees as far forward in front of you as you can. Your stomach and back naturally arch up a bit, and your head extends back, creating a stretch in the whole body. (2)

- As you exhale, allow your body to return to the original starting position. (3)

- Repeat twice more.

- Bring your right leg, near the ankle, on top of your left thigh just above the knee, letting the right leg open to the side. (4) Inhale, stretching forward as before, and exhale, releasing back, three times. (5)

- Bring the right leg down, placing the sole flat on the floor.

- Bring the left leg on top of the right thigh, and stretch as above, three times.

- Bring the left leg down, placing the sole flat on the floor.

- Inhale, stretching both knees forward, and "walk" your hands forward until your knees come to the floor (you're now sitting in seiza position with your toes bent under you). (6) Brush from the left shoulder down the left arm three times. (6, 7) Brush from the right shoulder down the right arm three times.

- Brush from the kidneys down the thighs to the knees, continuing down the legs to the toes, then up the soles of the feet and back to the kidneys, twice. (8, 9, 10)

- Again brush from the kidneys, but this time when you reach the toes, rock back onto your feet and stand up, brushing from the toes up the front of the legs as you come to standing. (11)

- The hands come back to back when they reach the hara, and continue brushing up the midline of the body to overhead, then the arms open out and down, as you lower them to the sides. (12, 13, 14)

- Stand comfortably.

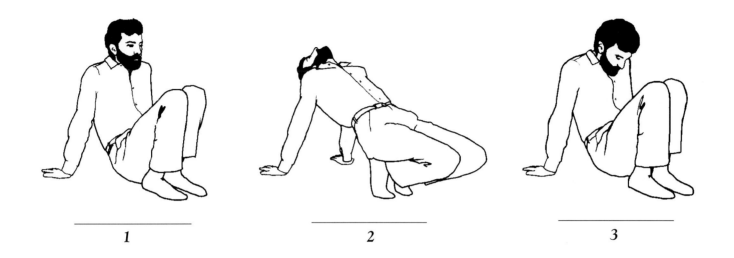

1   2   3

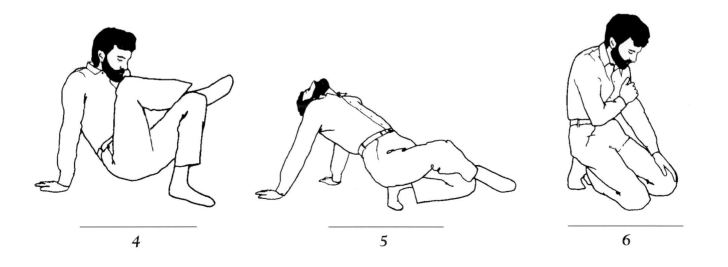

4   5   6

<u>Dropping the Load</u>
167

Continued ⟶

- *Brush from the left shoulder down the left arm three times. (6, 7) Brush from the right shoulder down the right arm three times.*

- *Brush from the kidneys down the thighs to the knees, continuing down the legs to the toes, then up the soles of the feet and back to the kidneys, twice. (8, 9, 10)*

- *Again brush from the kidneys, but this time when you reach the toes, rock back onto your feet and stand up, brushing from the toes up the front of the legs as you come to standing. (11)*

- *The hands come back to back when they reach the hara, and continue brushing up the midline of the body to overhead, then the arms open out and down, as you lower them to the sides. (12, 13, 14)*

- *Stand comfortably.*

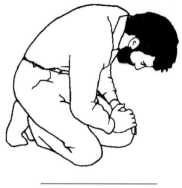

7

11

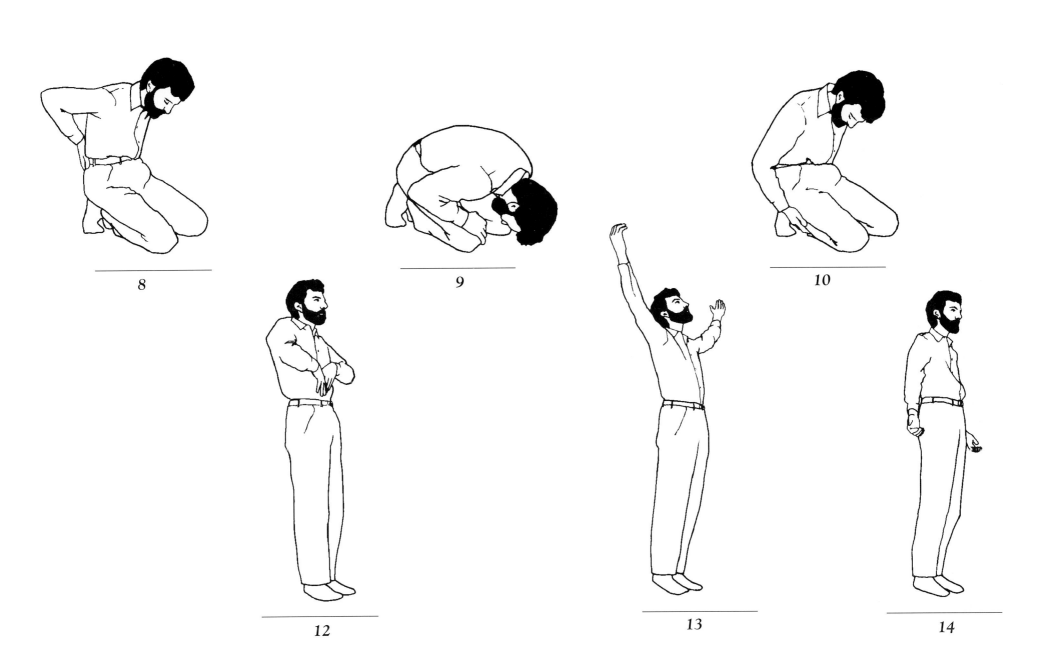

8

9

10

12

13

14

Palming the Eyes

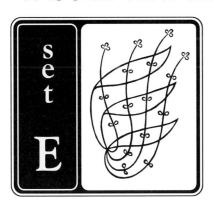

IT IS SAID THAT THE EYES ARE THE MIRROR OF THE "SOUL." MOST OF US HAVE GIVEN A LOT more attention to cleaning our mirror, which we may use twice a day, than to our eyes, which we use every waking moment. The eyes are especially stressed and weakened by television, constant reading, driving, desk and computer work, air pollutants, and lack of exposure to natural sunlight, as well as by the absence of natural color and impressions, such as those supplied by looking at a green hillside. Whatever you take in with your eyes is food for your whole body, as well as for your mind and emotions. It is well worth taking some time to make your surroundings pleasing to your eyes. This can mean the addition of plants or flowers to your room, hanging a favorite rug or painting on the wall, or placing a few beautiful objects on your desk. It certainly means keeping your environment clean and organized. The time it takes you to do so is a most worthwhile investment. Your eyes will be eating nurturing, balanced food, and your health and outlook on life will improve.

This exercise releases tension in the eyes and in the facial muscles surrounding the eyes. It's tremendously beneficial for people who have eye problems or poor eyesight. Anyone who reads or drives daily needs this exercise. The eyes are connected to the internal organs via the meridian system, and so Palming the Eyes is of great benefit to the liver. Everyone who is subject to pollution, crowded urban conditions, and food that has not been grown organically, needs this exercise. It can be done several times a day, as it is totally nurturing, rather than stimulating. Similar exercises have been developed in other health disciplines, such as Tai-Chi and Yoga, because the importance of relaxed, alert eyes for the health of the whole body has long been recognized.

Palming the Eyes

This exercise can be done standing, sitting on the floor, or sitting in a chair. Once you know how to do it, keep your eyes closed throughout the exercise.

- Bring the hands palm to palm in front of the body at heart level. (1)

- Rub the palms together rapidly, generating heat in your palms, and keeping your shoulders and arms relaxed.

- Closing your eyes, place the palms over the eyes so that they snugly contact the cheekbones, eye sockets, and bridge of the nose, shutting out all light. The hands are relaxed, and the fingers mold to the contours of the forehead. (2)

- Hold like this for three full breaths.

- Brush the hands up the forehead, over the crown of the head, down the back of the neck, and off below the chin. (3, 4, 5)

- Repeat the rubbing, palming and brushing two more times.

- The third and final time, continue brushing down the front of the body until the hands come to rest on the thighs (if sitting) or at your sides (if standing). (6)

- Slowly open the eyes, allowing them to remain unfocused for several seconds.

1

2

3

4

5

6

Kidney Charge

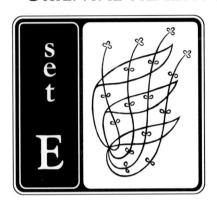

ORIENTAL HEALTH PHILOSOPHY SAYS THAT THE KIDNEYS, BY WHICH THE ANCIENTS MEANT both kidneys and adrenal glands, are the storehouse of the body's energy reserves. Affecting reproductive energy and governing resistance to mental, emotional, and physical stress are two of the key functions of this important organ. The kidneys are also active in preserving the body's water volume and achieving a constant salt/water balance. They detoxify and purify the blood, conserving essential elements and eliminating wastes in order to maintain chemical balances and energy for the body.

In addition to these functions, the adrenal glands are directly responsible for supplying energy when the body is in a state of emergency, and are involved in regulating the body's immune system.

High levels of tension and stress deplete the adrenals of energy and essential hormone products. This depletion can manifest as weakness, exhaustion, nervousness, fearfulness, irritability, backache, and higher susceptibility to colds and infections. Almost everyone in the Western world suffers from some degree of adrenal depletion, due to the constant overstimulation of modern living.

Strengthening weak kidneys and adrenals needs to be done in a nurturing rather than a stimulating manner. This exercise helps rebuild both the kidneys and adrenals by energizing them without the overstimulation that eventually leads to exhaustion. Because it nurtures the kidneys, it is extremely benefical to do Kidney Charge daily. Often the release of tension and an energizing effect can be experienced immediately.

Kidney Charge

INSTRUCTIONS

- Sit comfortably in cross-legged position. (1)

- Bring the soles of the feet together in front of the body. (2)

- With clustered fingertips, tap around the ankle bones of both feet, alternating left hand, right hand, etc. (3, 4, 5, 6)

- Continue for three breaths.

- Bring the thumbs to the balls of the feet at the Kidney 1 point, with fingers wrapped over the tops of the feet. (7, 8)

- On inhalation, stretch up and back, straightening the spine and arching the lower back while opening the soles towards the ceiling (edges of feet stay connected). (9)

- On exhalation, release the stretch, allowing the body to "collapse" forward, totally relaxed. (10)

- Repeat the stretch and release twice more.

- Brush the hands up the legs to the kidneys.

- Lean forward, and vigorously slap the kidneys with alternating open palms for three breaths. (11, 12, 13)

- Brush from the kidneys down the outside of the legs to the toes, three times. (14, 15)

- Holding the toes, bring one leg, then the other, back to cross-legged position. (16)

- Brush the hands to the knees. (17)

- Sit comfortably.

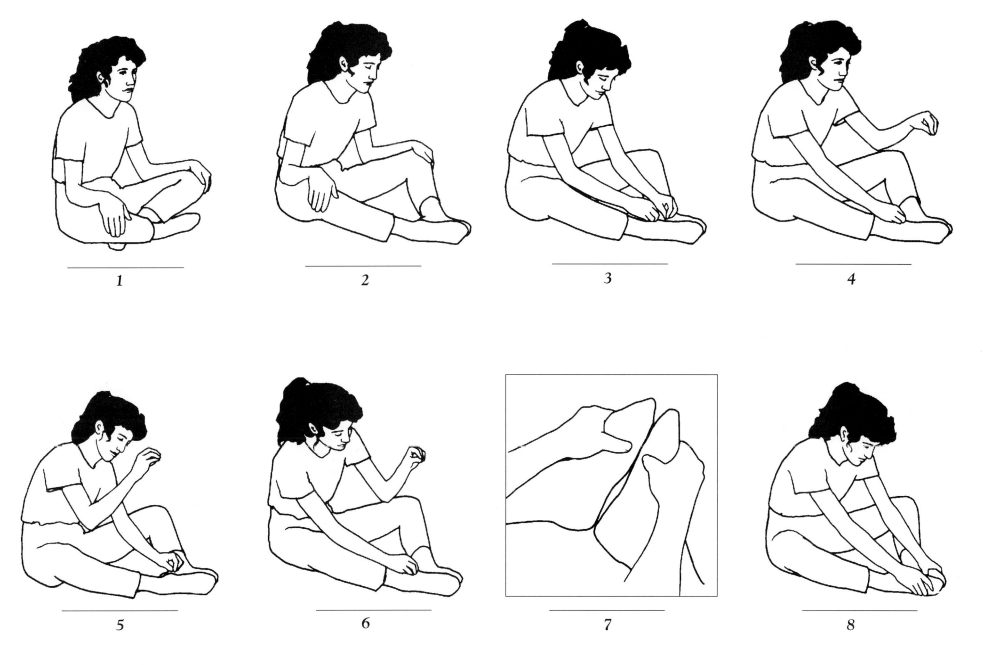

1

2

3

4

5

6

7

8

Continued ⟶

- *On inhalation, stretch up and back, straightening the spine and arching the lower back while opening the soles towards the ceiling (edges of feet stay connected). (9)*

- *On exhalation, release the stretch, allowing the body to "collapse" forward, totally relaxed. (10)*

- *Repeat the stretch and release twice more.*

- *Brush the hands up the legs to the kidneys.*

- *Lean forward, and vigorously slap the kidneys with alternating open palms for three breaths. (11, 12, 13)*

- *Brush from the kidneys down the outside of the legs to the toes, three times. (14, 15)*

- *Holding the toes, bring one leg, then the other, back to cross-legged position. (16)*

- *Brush the hands to the knees. (17)*

- *Sit comfortably.*

9

10

15

16

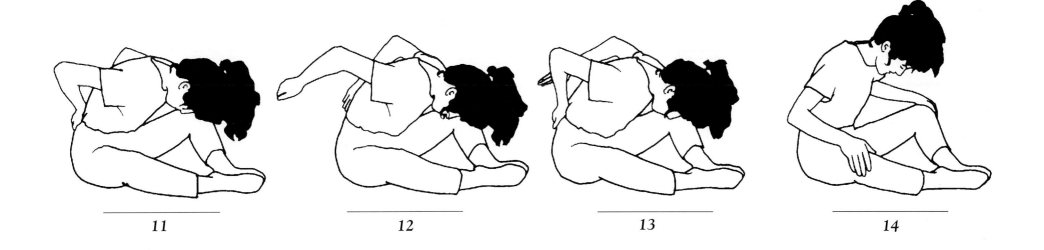

11   12   13   14

17

APPLYING SELF-BREEMA TO COMMON HEALTH PROBLEMS

Remember the blind man they took to Buddha? They said, "Buddha, he wishes to see, so we brought him to you." He replied, "Thank you for bringing him. Now please take him to the doctor!"

Although the beneficial effects of Self-Breema go far beyond simple physiotherapeutics, they can also be used to great advantage as a support in healing a variety of health problems. In actual fact, every Self-Breema exercise can positively influence (at least to some degree) any health problem. This is because Self-Breema works with the body as an energy system. Approached from an energy perspective, every single cell in the body, and every single metabolic process of each cell affects all the other cells in the body and their myriad functions. In other words, there is *one energy*, which influences and is influenced by every life process of the body, no matter how small or remote.

Why is this important? Prevalent medical thought tends to separate and divide the body into smaller and more isolated parts. Illness is attributed to the malfunction of a part or subsystem. When an *isolated* part is "sick," of course, there is no alternative but to "treat" it from the outside, with drugs, surgery, or some other form of unnatural manipulation.

But when the body is understood as an energy system, both localized and systemic malfunctions can usually be remedied by altering the quality and/or quantity of energy available to the entire system. This strengthening or purifying input can come through any accessible physical or energetic portal of the body. So a kidney problem can be positively affected by working with the feet, head, low back, by nutritional means, or by reaching a more balanced mental or emotional state. This, of course, does not obviate the need for the commonsense application of modern medicine. No one can dispute that there are conditions for which drugs, surgery, or high technology medical care are totally appropriate.

Still, you need to maintain an active posture, even when applying to others for help. *You* reach for help. *You* are the one who must know whether you have indeed been helped.

The Breema method views the body as a garden. Your job is to be the gardener. A good gardener knows when to water, when to prune, what tools to use, what foods and fertilizers are necessary, when to ask for advice or help from more experienced gardeners, and when to leave the garden alone and let Nature do her work. No matter how vibrant and beautiful the garden, it never reaches a stage where it ceases to require attention. Its very nature is that of dynamic balance through constant change.

The most successful approach to your day-to-day health is to work with the body as an energy system, and avoid getting lost in the microscopic viewpoint, "missing the forest for the trees." If you use these principles to maintain an accurate perspective, you can benefit by working with Self-Breema to help you through the following commonly encountered conditions. Each condition is followed by an alphabetical list of particularly appropriate Self-Breema exercises. Those exercises which usually have a more direct effect are marked with an asterisk.

HEADACHES
* Creating Flow
* Erasing the Page
* Palming the Eyes
* Tilling the Soil

ALLERGIES/ ASTHMA
* Erasing the Page
* Gushing Spring
* Kidney Charge
* Opening the Heart
  Pa ing the Eyes
  Touching the Source

COLDS/ CONGESTION
* Erasing the Page
  Evening Posture
  Giving to the Earth
* Gushing Spring
  Kidney Charge
* Opening the Heart
  Palming the Eyes
  Touching the Source

NECK AND SHOULDER ACHE

* Creating Flow
* Evening Posture
  Opening the Heart
* Palming the Eyes

MID-BACK ACHE

  Closing the Gate
* Dropping the Load
  Evening Posture
* Opening the Heart

DIGESTIVE PROBLEMS/ MENSTRUAL DIFFICULTIES

  Circling the Knee
  Dropping the Load
* Grinding the Wheat
* Harvesting the Resin
* Hulling the Walnut
* Touching the Mountain

LOW-BACK ACHE

* Circling the Knee
  Dancing on the Grapes
  Dropping the Load
* Giving to the Earth
* Grinding the Wheat
  Kidney Charge

DEPRESSION/ EMOTIONAL IMBALANCE

  Chasing the Arrow
  Fire Posture
* Gushing Spring
  Opening the Heart
* Palming the Eyes
* Tilling the Soil
  Touching the Source

FATIGUE

  Chasing the Arrow
  Dancing on the Grapes
* Erasing the Page
  Fire Posture
  Gushing Spring
* Kidney Charge
* Palming the Eyes
* Tilling the Soil

Table 1. Principal Physical Emphasis of the Exercises

		Head/Neck	Upper Back	Arms/Hands	Lower Back/Hips	Legs/Feet	Other
set A	Grinding the Wheat				•		
	Circling the Knee	•	•		•	•	
	Touching the Source			•			Chest
	Gushing Spring			•		•	Chest
set B	Chasing the Arrow			•	•		
	Harvesting the Resin				•	•	
	Touching the Mountain						Torso/Eyes
	Hulling the Walnut				•	•	
set C	Evening Posture	•	•				
	Dancing on the Grapes				•	•	
	Erasing the Page	•					Face
	Opening the Heart		•				
set D	Creating Flow	•	•				
	Fire Posture						Whole Body
	Tilling the Soil					•	
	Giving to the Earth				•	•	
set E	Closing the Gate			•	•		
	Dropping the Load			•		•	•
	Palming the Eyes	•					Eyes
	Kidney Charge				•	•	

Table 1
185

Alphabetical Index of Exercises

THE INSTITUTE FOR HEALTH IMPROVEMENT

The Institute for Health Improvement is a unique school that provides students the opportunity to develop a practical and profound understanding of the body. Students at the Institute gain knowledge of how to maintain and improve both their own and other people's health. The exposition and experience of the laws and principles of health are achieved by studying and practicing the Breema bodywork method.

The Institute is located at 309 62nd St., Oakland, California 94618, USA. Their telephone number is (415) 428-0937.

ABOUT THE AUTHOR Dr. Jon Schreiber, D.C., has been active in the field of health and human biology for many years. His concern with the limitations of traditional health care systems led him to study many alternative therapies. In Breema bodywork, he recognized a system unique in its dynamic ability to vitalize and heal the body, and he has been teaching this method for nine years. A Phi Beta Kappa graduate of Oberlin College, Dr. Schreiber graduated first in his class at Palmer College of Chiropractic. In addition to his active faculty and administrative roles at The Institute for Health Improvement, he directs Schreiber Chiropractic Natural Health Center, where he has used Breema bodywork as the primary means for helping thousands of people regain and improve their health. He also teaches the Breema method throughout the United States and abroad to health professionals.

Schreiber Chiropractic Natural Health Center is located at 6201 Florio St., Oakland, California 94618, USA. Their telephone number is (415) 428-1234.

This is when Mullah Nasser Eddin says, "After Enlightenment, move around a bit, shake your head a little, stretch your legs a bit. Maybe you are hungry, my boy!"